SYMBIOSIS the pearson custom library for the biological sciences

Lab Manual
BIOL 1407
Spring / Fall
Professor Betsy Morgan

Pearson Learning Solutions

New York   Boston   San Francisco
London   Toronto   Sydney   Tokyo   Singapore   Madrid
Mexico City   Munich   Paris   Cape Town   Hong Kong   Montreal

Senior Vice President, Editorial and Marketing: Patrick F. Boles
Senior Sponsoring Editor: Natalie Danner
Development Editor: Annette Fantasia
Editorial Assistant: Jill Johnson
Executive Marketing Manager: Nathan L. Wilbur
Operations Manager: Eric M. Kenney
Database Production Manager: Jennifer Berry
Art Director: Renée Sartell
Cover Designer: Kristen Kiley

Cover Art: Courtesy of Michael R. Martin, Darryl Johnson, Photodisk, DK Images, and Prentice-Hall, Inc.

Copyright © 2010 by Pearson Learning Solutions
All rights reserved.

Permission in writing must be obtained from the publisher before any part of this work may be reproduced or transmitted in any form or by any means, electronic or mechanical, including photocopying and recording, or by any information storage or retrieval system.

Additional copyright information is included, where applicable, as a footnote at the beginning of each chapter.

Pyrex, pHydrion, Chem3D Plus, Apple, Macintosh, Chemdraw, Hypercard, graphTool, Corning, Teflon, Mel-Temp, Rotaflow, Tygon, Spec20, and LambdaII UV/Vis are registered trademarks.

Chem3D Plus is a registered trademark of the Cambridge Soft Corp.

The information, illustrations, and/or software contained in this book, and regarding the above mentioned programs, are provided "as is," without warranty of any kind, express or implied, including without limitation any warranty concerning the accuracy, adequacy, or completeness of such information. Neither the publisher, the authors, nor the copyright holders shall be responsible for any claims attributable to errors, omissions, or other inaccuracies contained in this book. Nor shall they be liable for direct, indirect, special, incidental, or consequential damages arising out of the use of such information or material.

The authors and publisher believe that the lab experiments described in this publication, when conducted in conformity with the safety precautions described herein and according to the school's laboratory safety procedures, are reasonably safe for the students for whom this manual is directed. Nonetheless, many of the described experiments are accompanied by some degree of risk, including human error, the failure or misuse of laboratory or electrical equipment, mismeasurement, spills of chemicals, and exposure to sharp objects, heat, body fluids, blood or other biologics. The authors and publisher disclaim any liability arising from such risks in connections with any of the experiments contained in this manual. If students have questions or problems with materials, procedures, or instructions on any experiment, they should always ask their instructor for help before proceeding.

This special edition published in cooperation with Pearson Learning Solutions.

Printed in the United States of America.

V0UD

Please visit our web site at *www.pearsoncustom.com/*.

Attention bookstores: For permission to return unused stock, contact us at *pe-uscustomreturns@pearson.com*.

Pearson Learning Solutions, 501 Boylston Street, Suite 900, Boston, MA 02116
A Pearson Education Company
www.pearsoned.com

ISBN 10: 0-536-92488-0
ISBN 13: 978-0-536-92488-9

Laboratory Safety:
General Guidelines

1. Notify your instructor immediately if you are pregnant, color blind, allergic to any insects or chemicals, taking immunosuppressive drugs, or have any other medical condition (such as diabetes, immunologic defect) that may require special precautionary measures in the laboratory.

2. Upon entering the laboratory, place all books, coats, purses, backpacks, etc. in designated areas, not on the bench tops.

3. Locate and, when appropriate, learn to use exits, fire extinguisher, fire blanket, chemical shower, eyewash, first aid kit, broken glass container, and cleanup materials for spills.

4. In case of fire, evacuate the room and assemble outside the building.

5. Do not eat, drink, smoke, or apply cosmetics in the laboratory.

6. Confine long hair, loose clothing, and dangling jewelry.

7. Wear shoes at all times in the laboratory.

8. Cover any cuts or scrapes with a sterile, waterproof bandage before attending lab.

9. Wear eye protection when working with chemicals.

10. Never pipet by mouth. Use mechanical pipeting devices.

11. Wash skin immediately and thoroughly if contaminated by chemicals or microorganisms.

12. Do not perform unauthorized experiments.

13. Do not use equipment without instruction.

14. Report *all* spills and accidents to your instructor immediately.

15. Never leave heat sources unattended.

16. When using hot plates, note that there is no visible sign that they are hot (such as a red glow). Always assume that hot plates are hot.

17. Use an appropriate apparatus when handling hot glassware.

18. Keep chemicals away from direct heat or sunlight.

19. Keep containers of alcohol, acetone, and other flammable liquids away from flames.

20. Do not allow any liquid to come into contact with electrical cords. Handle electrical connectors with dry hands. Do not attempt to disconnect electrical equipment that crackles, snaps, or smokes.

21. Upon completion of laboratory exercises, place all materials in the disposal areas designated by your instructor.

22. Do not pick up broken glassware with your hands. Use a broom and dustpan and discard the glass in designated glass waste containers; never discard with paper waste.

23. Wear disposable gloves when working with blood, other body fluids, or mucous membranes. Change gloves after possible contamination and wash hands immediately after gloves are removed.

24. The disposal symbol indicates that items that may have come in contact with body fluids should be placed in your lab's designated container. It also refers to liquid wastes that should not be poured down the drain into the sewage system.

25. Leave the laboratory clean and organized for the next student.

26. Wash your hands with liquid or powdered soap prior to leaving the laboratory.

27. The biohazard symbol indicates procedures that may pose health concerns.

The caution symbol points out instruments, substances, and procedures that require special attention to safety. These symbols appear throughout this manual.

Measurement Conversions

Metric to American Standard	American Standard to Metric
Length	
1 mm = 0.039 inches	1 inch = 2.54 cm
1 cm = 0.394 inches	1 foot = 0.305 m
1 m = 3.28 feet	1 yard = 0.914 m
1 m = 1.09 yards	1 mile = 1.61 km
Volume	
1 mL = 0.0338 fluid ounces	1 fluid ounce = 29.6 mL
1 L = 4.23 cups	1 cup = 237 mL
1 L = 2.11 pints	1 pint = 0.474 L
1 L = 1.06 quarts	1 quart = 0.947 L
1 L = 0.264 gallons	1 gallon = 3.79 L
Mass	
1 mg = 0.0000353 ounces	1 ounce = 28.3 g
1 g = 0.0353 ounces	1 pound = 0.454 kg
1 kg = 2.21 pounds	

Temperature

To convert temperature:

$$^\circ C = \frac{5}{9}(F - 32) \qquad ^\circ F = \frac{9}{5}C + 32$$

Contents

Protists and Fungi

 This lab topic gives you the opportunity to practice the scientific process. Before going to lab, carefully read through this lab exercise. Be prepared to use this information to design an experiment with protists or fungi.

Laboratory Objectives

After completing this lab topic, you should be able to:

1. Discuss the diversity of protists and fungi, and the current interest in their phylogenetic relationships.
2. Describe the diversity of protists, explaining the means of obtaining nutrition and method of locomotion for each group.
3. Identify representative organisms in several major protistan phyla.
4. Discuss the ecological role and economic importance of protists.
5. Describe the characteristics and representative organisms of the green algae and their relationship to land plants.
6. Describe the divisions of the kingdom Fungi, recognizing and identifying representative organisms in each.
7. Describe differences in reproduction in fungal phyla.
8. Discuss the ecological role and economic importance of fungi.
9. Design and perform an independent investigation of a protist or an organism in the kingdom Fungi.

Introduction

Unicellular eukaryotic organisms originated over 2 billion years ago, and today they are found in every habitable region of Earth. The enormous diversity of organisms, their numerous adaptations, and their cellular complexity reflect the long evolutionary history of eukaryotes. For almost 30 years, scientists placed these diverse groups of unicellular organisms into the kingdom Protista. The Protista usually included all organisms not placed in the other eukaryotic kingdoms of Plants, Animals, and Fungi. This catchall kingdom included not only the unicellular eukaryotes, but also their multicellular relatives, like the giant kelps and seaweeds. However, most scientists now agree that the kingdom Protista should be divided into several kingdoms within the domain Eukarya, each reflecting a single evolution-

From *Investigating Biology*, Fourth Edition, Judith Giles Morgan and M. Eloise Brown Carter. Copyright © 2002 Pearson Education, Inc., publishing as Benjamin Cummings. All rights reserved.

ary origin. Some propose six eukaryotic kingdoms, others propose more. In this lab topic we will refer to this diverse group as **protists** (a general term, not a taxonomic category), leaving open the final designation of kingdoms.

The most familiar protists, algae and protozoans, have been well studied since the earliest development of the microscope. Therefore, one might assume that the taxonomic relationships among the various protistans are well understood. However, the phylogeny (evolutionary history) of these groups has been difficult to determine from comparisons of cell structure and function, nutrition, and reproduction. Evolutionary biology and taxonomy are branches of science in which many of the interesting "experiments" occurred millions or even billions of years ago. Scientists cannot repeat these evolutionary "experiments," but they can use multiple sources of evidence to determine which groups of organisms have features in common and therefore represent a single phylogenetic group. Recent molecular and biochemical research, particularly the ability to sequence ribosomal and transfer RNA genes, has provided strong new evidence for reconstructing the relationships of the protists. The results of this work have challenged not only the five-kingdom classification scheme, but also our definition of a kingdom. Some of the evidence is contradictory, requiring further testing. These investigations into the nature of eukaryotic diversity demonstrate the process of scientific inquiry. New technologies, new ideas, and novel experiments are used to test hypotheses, and the resulting evidence must be consistent with the existing body of knowledge and our classification scheme. The results lead to modification of our hypotheses and further research.

Some students may find the changing classification within the protists frustrating, but you should try to view this as the hallmark of science. Even the concept of the kingdom can be challenged and changed in response to new evidence. No matter how many kingdoms are proposed, remember that this is a reflection of the evolution of eukaryotes over the rich history of the earth. It is not surprising that the diversity of life does not easily fit into our constructed categories.

If you complete all of the lab topics in this laboratory manual, you will have studied examples of all the major groups of organisms with the exception of those in domain Archaea. You will investigate plant evolution and animal evolution in subsequent lab topics. In this lab topic, you will survey the diversity of protists in several phyla, with particular attention to nutrition, locomotion, and cellular complexity. (The designations *phylum* and *division* are equivalent taxonomic groupings and we will use phylum when referring to protists and fungi. Zoologists traditionally used *phylum*, while botanists used *division*. However, both terms now are accepted by the Botanical Code for Nomenclature.) You will continue your investigation of diversity with the Fungi, a kingdom composed of multicellular, heterotrophic eukaryotes that absorb their food.

At the end of this lab topic you will be asked to design a simple experiment to further your investigation of the behavior, ecology, or physiology of one of the organisms studied. As you proceed through the exercises, ask questions about your observations and consider an experiment that you might design to answer one question.

EXERCISE 1
The Protists

In this exercise you will investigate the diversity of organisms traditionally considered protists. To organize your study, protists can be divided into three categories (not taxonomic groups) according to their mode of nutrition. The *protozoa* are **heterotrophic** protists that ingest their food by **phagocytosis** (the uptake of large particles or whole organisms by the pinching inward of the plasma membrane). Some protozoa, euglenoids for example, are **mixotrophic,** capable of photosynthesis and ingestion. The *algae* include all photosynthetic (**autotrophic**) unicellular organisms and their multicellular relatives. Traditionally, dinoflagellates have been considered algae, but recent evidence suggests that they are closely related to the protozoa, specifically ciliates. The green algae are included in the protists, although, as you will see, evidence indicates that land plants originated from ancestral green algae, and some classifications place green algae (or at least those known as charophytes) in the kingdom Plantae. The third category includes the *funguslike slime molds* that are heterotrophic, obtaining their nutrition by absorbing nutrients from decomposing organic material. Some scientists propose placing the slime molds in a separate kingdom, Mycetozoa, a name that reflects their close relationship with fungi (*myco*) and animals (*zoa*).

These three general categories—protozoa, algae, and slime molds—provide a framework for the study of the diverse organisms referred to as protists. For each organism that you investigate, you will find a brief statement about protistan classification that incorporates molecular and cytological evidence. (For further discussion of protistan classification, see Campbell and Reece, 2002.)

Lab Study A. Heterotrophic Protists—Protozoa

Materials

compound microscope
slides and coverslips
prepared slides of foraminiferans
prepared slides of radiolarians
   skeletons (demonstration only)
prepared slides of
   Trypanosoma levisi
cultures of living
   Paramecium caudata
Protoslo® or other quieting agent

solution of yeast stained with
   Congo red
cultures of *Paramecium caudata*
   that have been fed yeast stained
   with Congo red (optional)
dropper bottle of 1% acetic acid
transfer pipettes
freshwater and marine
   plankton tows

Introduction

Traditionally, single-celled heterotrophic protists are called *protozoa.* There are three categories of protozoa based on their mode of locomotion. In one group, organisms move and feed using cellular extensions called **pseudopodia.** Included in this group are amoebas, foraminiferans, and actinopods. Other protozoa move using **flagella,** motile structures supported by microtubules. The third means of locomotion in protozoa is by **cilia,** short cellular extensions supported by microtubules.

Protozoa That Move Using Pseudopodia

Although some taxonomists group all protists that move using pseudopodia into one phylum, others divide the group into several phyla. Given the present uncertainty of the protistan classification, we have selected three protozoans with pseudopodia that were traditionally in different phyla.

Rhizopods (Amoebas)

The rhizopod *Amoeba proteus* is a protozoan species of organisms that move using **pseudopodia**. Rhizopod is derived from *rhizo* or root and *pod* or foot; thus, rootlike foot. In this group, organisms have no fixed body shape, and they are naked; that is, they do not have a shell. Different species may be found in a variety of habitats, including freshwater and marine habitats. Recall that pseudopodia are cellular extensions. As the pseudopod extends, endoplasm flows into the extension. By extending several pseudopods in sequence and flowing into first one and then the next, the amoeba proceeds along in an irregular, slow fashion. Pseudopods are also used to capture and ingest food. When a suitable food particle such as a bacterium, another protist, or a piece of detritus (fragmented remains of dead organisms) contacts an amoeba, a pseudopod will flow completely around the particle and take it into the cell by phagocytosis.

Foraminiferans (Forams)

Foraminiferans, commonly called **forams,** are another example of organisms that move and feed using pseudopodia. Forams are marine planktonic (freely floating) or benthic (bottom-dwelling) organisms that secrete a shell-like *test* (a hard outer covering) made up of chambers. In many species, the test consists of chambers secreted in a spiral pattern, and the organism resembles a microscopic snail. Although most forams are microscopic, some species, called *living sands,* may grow to the size of several centimeters, an astounding size for a single-celled protist. Pseudopodia extend through special pores in the calcium carbonate test. The test can persist after the organism dies, becoming part of marine sand. Remains of tests can form vast limestone deposits.

Procedure

1. Obtain a prepared slide of representative forams (Figure 1a).
2. Observe the organisms first on the lowest power of the compound microscope and then on intermediate and high powers.
3. Note the arrangement and attempt to count the number of chambers in the test. In most species, the number of chambers indicates the relative ages of the organisms, with older organisms having more chambers. Which are more abundant on your slide, older or younger organisms?

   Chambers can be arranged in a single row, in multiple rows, or wound into a spiral. Protozoologists determine the foram species based on the appearance of the test. Are different species present?

Results

Sketch several different forams in the margin of your lab manual. Note differences in the organisms on your slide and those depicted in Figure 1a.

4

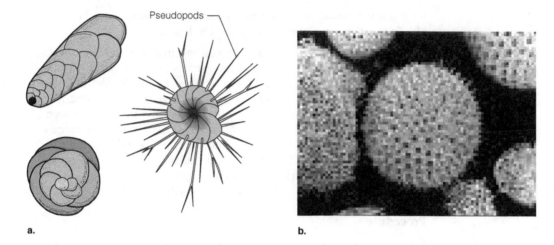

Pseudopods

a.

b.

Figure 1.
Heterotrophic organisms (protozoa) that move using pseudopodia. (a)
Forams have a shell-like test made of calcium carbonate. Slender pseudopods
extend through pores in the test. (b) Radiolarians are supported by a skeleton of
silicon dioxide.

Actinopods (Radiolarians)

Actinopods have pseudopodia that are supported by a bundle of microtubules forming very slender **axopodia**. The **radiolarians** studied here are
common in marine plankton. They secrete skeletons of silicon dioxide that
can, as with the forams, collect in vast deposits on the ocean floor. The
axopodia extend outward through pores in the skeleton in all directions
from the central spherical cell body.

Procedure

1. Observe slides of radiolarians on demonstration.
2. Observe the size and shape of the skeletons and compare your observations with Figure 1b.

Results

Sketch several different radiolarians skeletons in the margin of your lab
manual, noting any differences between the organisms on demonstration
and those in the figure.

Protozoa That Move Using Flagella

Flagellates are generally single-celled, heterotrophic protists. They may be
free-living and parasitic, or they may live in symbiotic relationships with
other organisms. The many diverse single-celled and colonial flagellates
have been a particular challenge to taxonomists. Under the old two-kingdom
system of classification, the heterotrophic flagellates were classified as animals, and the autotrophic flagellates (with chloroplasts) were classified
as plants. However, the well-defined taxonomic group of flagellates, the
euglenoids, has members of each type, and some members are mixotrophic,
depending on their environment. Recent classification changes proposed

for flagellates would place euglenoids together with symbiotic flagellates, like *Trypanosoma,* in a new category, the **Euglenozoa.**

The heterotrophic organisms that you investigate in this exercise move using one or more flagella, long cytoplasmic extensions supported by a nine-doublet of microtubules surrounding a single central doublet of microtubules. In this exercise, you will observe a flagellate, *Trypanosoma levisi.* Organisms in the genus *Trypanosoma* are parasites that alternate between a vertebrate and an invertebrate host. *Trypanosoma levisi* lives in the blood of rats and is transmitted by fleas. Its flagellum originates near the posterior end but passes to the front end as a marginal thread of a long undulating membrane. Another organism in this same genus, *T. gambiense,* causes African sleeping sickness in humans. Its invertebrate host is the tsetse fly.

Procedure

1. Obtain a prepared slide of *T. levisi* (Figure 2) and observe it, using low, intermediate, and high powers in the compound microscope.
2. Locate the organisms among the blood cells of the parasite's host.
3. Identify the **flagellum,** the **undulating membrane,** and the **nucleus** in several organisms.

Figure 2.
Protozoa that move using flagella.
Trypanosoma is a parasite that lives in the blood of its mammalian host. The flagellum originates near the posterior end but passes along an undulating membrane to the anterior end.

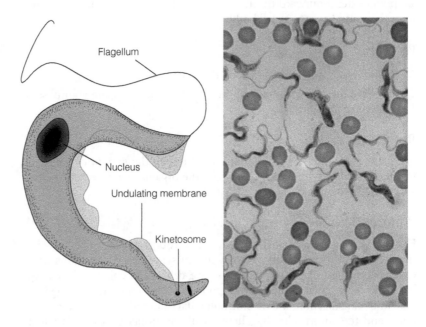

Flagellum

Nucleus

Undulating membrane

Kinetosome

Results

In the margin of your lab manual, draw several representative examples of *T. levisi* and several blood cells to show relative cell sizes.

Protozoa That Move Using Cilia

Protozoans in this category move using cilia, short projections from the cell surface. Cilia are generally shorter and more numerous than flagella. Internally, both structures are similar in their core of a nine-doublet of microtubules surrounding a single central doublet of microtubules. Proposed groupings of protistans place ciliates and dinoflagellates (Lab Study B) into a new taxonomic category, the **Alveolata.** Members of the Alveolata have small subsurface membrane-bound cavities called **alveoli.** Until there is a consensus, we have included ciliates with the protozoans and the dinoflagellates with the algae. In this activity, you will observe the ciliate *Paramecium caudatum.*

Procedure

1. Using the compound microscope, examine a living *Paramecium*. Place a drop of water from the bottom of the culture on a clean microscope slide. Add a *small* drop of Protoslo or some other quieting solution to the water drop; then add the coverslip.

2. Observe paramecia on the compound microscope using low and then intermediate powers.

3. Describe the movement of a single paramecium. Does movement appear to be directional or is it random? Does the organism reverse direction only when it encounters an object, or does it appear to reverse direction even with no obstruction?

4. Locate a large, slowly moving organism, switch to high power, and identify the following organelles:

    Oral groove: depression in the side of the cell that runs obliquely back to the mouth that opens into a **gullet.**

    Food vacuole: forms at the end of the gullet. Food vacuoles may appear as dark vesicles throughout the cell.

    Macronucleus: large, grayish body in the center of the cell. The macronucleus has many copies of the genome and controls most cellular activities, including asexual reproduction.

    Micronucleus: often difficult to see in living organisms, this small round body may be lying close to the macronucleus. Micronuclei are involved in sexual reproduction. Many species of paramecia have more than one micronucleus.

    Contractile vacuole: used for water balance, two of these form, one at each end of the cell. Each contractile vacuole is made up of a ring of radiating tubules and a central spherical vacuole. Your organism may be under osmotic stress because of the Protoslo, and the contractile vacuoles may be filling and collapsing as they expel water from the cell.

5. Observe feeding in a paramecium. Add a drop of yeast stained with Congo red to the edge of the coverslip and watch as it diffuses around the paramecium.

    Study the movement of food particles from the oral groove to the gullet to the formation of a food vacuole that will subsequently move through the cell as the food is digested in the vacuole. You may be able to observe the discharge of undigested food from the food vacuole at a specific site on the cell surface.

6. Observe the discharge of **trichocysts,** structures that lie just under the outer surface of the paramecium. When irritated by a chemical or attacked by a predator, the paramecium discharges these long thin threads that may serve as a defense mechanism, as an anchoring device, or to capture prey. Make a new slide of paramecia. Add a drop of 1% acetic acid to the edge of the coverslip and carefully watch a paramecium. Describe the appearance of trichocysts in this species.

Results

Complete the drawing of a paramecium below, labeling all the organelles and structures shown in bold in the text.

Discussion

1. Describe the mechanism for feeding in amoeboid, flagellated, and ciliated protozoans.

2. How do you think amoeboid organisms with skeletons, such as the radiolarians, move food to their cell bodies?

3. Compare the appearance and rate of locomotion in amoeboid, flagellated, and ciliated organisms observed in this exercise.

4. Describe mechanisms for defense in the organisms studied.

5. Give examples of modifications in cell shape or distribution of cilia or flagella allowing the organism to adapt to its environment.

6. Complete Table 1, summarizing characteristics of organisms in the heterotrophic protistan phyla.

Table 1
Characteristics of Heterotrophic Protists—Protozoa

Group	Nutritional Mode	Means of Locomotion	Protective Adaptations	Habitat or Lifestyle	Other Unusual Characteristics
Rhizopods					
Foraminiferans					
Actinopods					
Flagellates					
Ciliates					

Lab Study B. Autotrophic Protists—Algae

Materials

compound microscope
slides and coverslips
living cultures or prepared slides
   of dinoflagellates
living cultures of diatoms
prepared slides of diatomaceous
   earth, demonstration only

marine plankton samples
transfer pipettes for all cultures
demonstration materials of
   brown algae and red algae

Introduction

In this lab study you will investigate representatives of four phyla of algae. Body form, flagella, and photosynthetic pigments can distinguish the algae. In **unicellular** organisms, the body is only one cell, and daughter cells separate from each other after division. In **filamentous** organisms, cell division takes place in the same plane, and the daughter cells remain attached, resulting in a long line of cells—a filament. Whereas **aggregates** are random, temporary clusters of cells, **simple** and **complex colonies** are predictable organizations of cells either without physiological connections (a simple colony) or with them (a complex colony). In aggregates, simple colonies, and complex colonies, cell divisions take place in many planes. The complex bodies of **multicellular** algae are differentiated into specialized structures for photosynthesis, flotation, and anchorage.

The phyla of algae are characterized by differences in cellular structure and pigmentation. The exclusively microscopic algae demonstrate differences in cell walls (diatoms) and flagella (dinoflagellates). All the algae have chlorophyll *a* as their primary photosynthetic pigment, but brown and red algae have additional accessory pigments. Green algae, like land plants, have chlorophyll *b* as an accessory pigment. Accessory pigments increase the spectrum of light available for photosynthesis. This is particularly important for aquatic organisms because many wavelengths of light, including those absorbed by chlorophyll *a*, are absorbed as they pass through ocean waters. Finally, the red algae lack flagella at any stage in their life cycle. In this lab study, you will examine some of the most common and ecologically important protistan algae, learning the characteristics, ecological roles, and economic importance of each.

Dinoflagellates (Dinoflagellata)

Swirl your hand through tropical ocean waters at night, and you may notice a burst of tiny lights. Visit a warm, stagnant inlet and you might notice that the water appears reddish and dead fish are floating on the surface. Both of these phenomena may be due to activities of dinoflagellates, single-celled organisms that are generally photosynthetic. Some are able to bioluminesce, or produce light. They sometimes can *bloom* (reproduce very rapidly) and cause the water to appear red from pigments in their bodies. If the organisms in this "red tide" are a species of dinoflagellate that releases toxins, fish and other marine animals can be poisoned. Red tides in the Chesapeake Bay are thought to be caused by *Pfiesteria,* a dinoflagellate that produces deadly toxins resulting in invertebrate and fish kills, and that also may be implicated in human illness and death. Dinoflagellates have a cellulose cell wall that is often in the form of an armor of numerous plates with two perpendicular

a. Dinoflagellates

b. Diatoms

Figure 3.

Autotrophic protists (algae). (a) Dinoflagellates have a cellulose cell wall in the form of plates with two grooves that house flagella. (b) Diatoms have a cell wall made of silica consisting of two valves. Species can be pennate forms or centric forms.

grooves, each containing a flagellum. These organisms play an important role in **primary productivity** in oceans, photosynthesis that ultimately provides food for all marine organisms.

Dinoflagellates have traditionally been considered algae, but as previously mentioned, they are now thought to share a common ancestor with ciliates, as evidenced by the presence of subsurface cavities called alveoli. In the future, dinoflagellates and ciliates may be placed in a single group, the Alveolata.

Procedure

1. Obtain a prepared slide or make a wet mount of dinoflagellates (Figure 3a).
2. Focus the slide on low power and attempt to locate the cells. You may have to switch to intermediate power to see them.
3. Switch to high power.
4. Identify the perpendicular **grooves** and the **cellulose plates** making up the cell wall. Are the plates in your species elongated into spines? **Flagella** may be visible in living specimens.

Results

1. Draw several examples of cell shapes in the margin of your lab manual. Note differences between the species on your slide and those in Figure 3a.

2. Summarize distinguishing characteristics of dinoflagellates.

3. Describe the ecological role and economic importance of these organisms.

Diatoms (Bacillariophyta)

Diatoms also play an important role in primary productivity in oceans. In fact, they are the most important photosynthesizers in cold marine waters. They can be unicellular, or they can aggregate into chains or starlike groups. Protoplasts of these organisms are enclosed by a cell wall made of silica that persists after the death of the cell. These cell wall deposits are mined as **diatomaceous earth** and have numerous economic uses, for example, in swimming pool filters and as an abrasive in toothpaste and silver polish. Perhaps the greatest value of diatoms, however, is the excess carbohydrate and oxygen they produce that can be utilized by other organisms. Ecologists are concerned about the effects of acid rain and changing climatic conditions on populations of diatoms and their rate of primary productivity.

Diatom cells are either elongated, boat-shaped, bilaterally symmetrical **pennate** forms or radially symmetrical **centric** forms. The cell wall consists of two valves, one fitting inside the other, in the manner of the lid and bottom of a petri dish. As scientists continue to utilize new information in classifying the protists, the diatoms, brown algae (in the next section), and golden algae (not included in this lab topic) are placed in a single group, **Stramenopila,** based on unique flagella structure usually observed in sex cells.

Procedure

1. Prepare a wet mount of diatoms (Figure 3b) from marine plankton samples or other living cultures.
2. Observe the organisms on low, intermediate, and high powers.
3. Describe the form of the diatoms in your sample. Are they centric, pennate, or both?

4. If you are studying living cells, you may be able to detect locomotion. The method of movement is uncertain, but it is thought that contractile fibers just inside the cell membrane produce waves of motion on the cytoplasmic surface that extends through a groove in the cell wall. What is the body form of motile diatoms?

5. Observe a single centric form on high power and note the intricate geometric pattern of the cell wall. Can you detect the two valves?
6. Look for chloroplasts in living forms.

7. Observe diatomaceous earth on demonstration and identify pennate and centric forms.

Results

1. Sketch several different shapes of diatoms in the margin of your lab manual.
2. Summarize distinguishing characteristics of diatoms.

3. Describe the ecological role and economic importance of these organisms.

Discussion

1. Compare dinoflagellates and diatoms. What important ecological role is shared by these two groups?

2. What is one characteristic that you could observe under the microscope to distinguish diatoms and dinoflagellates?

Brown Algae (Phaeophyta)

Some of the largest algae, the **kelps,** are brown algae. The Sargasso Sea is named after the large, free-floating brown algae *Sargassum.* These algae appear brown because of the presence of the brown pigment **fucoxanthin** in addition to chlorophyll *a*. Brown algae are perhaps best known for their commercial value. Have you ever wondered why commercial ice cream is smoother in texture than homemade ice cream? Extracts of **algin,** a polysaccharide in the cell wall of some brown algae, are used commercially as thickening or emulsifying agents in paint, toothpaste, ice cream, pudding, and in many other commercial food products. *Laminaria,* known as *kombu* in Japan, is added to soups, used to brew a beverage, and covered with icing as a dessert. As previously noted, the brown algae and diatoms may share a common ancestor and therefore be placed together in the Stramenopila.

Procedure

Observe the examples of brown algae that are on demonstration.

Results

In Table 2 on the next page, list the names and distinguishing characteristics of each brown algal species on demonstration. Compare the examples with those illustrated in Figure 4.

Table 2
Representative Brown Algae

Name	Body Form (single-celled, filamentous, colonial, leaflike; broad or linear blades)	Characteristics (pigments, reproductive structures, structures for attachment and flotation)

Red Algae (Rhodophyta)

The simplest red algae are single-celled, but most species have a macroscopic, multicellular body form. The red algae, unlike all the other algae, do not have flagella at any stage in their life cycle. Some scientists suggest that the red algae represent a monophyletic (having a single origin) group and should be placed in their own kingdom. Red algae contain chlorophyll *a* and the accessory pigments **phycocyanin** and **phycoerythrin** that often mask the chlorophyll, making the algae appear red. These pigments absorb

Figure 4.

Examples of multicellular brown algae (phylum Phaeophyta). The body of a brown alga consists of a broad **blade,** a stemlike **stipe,** and a **holdfast** for attachment. These body parts are found in the kelps (a) *Laminaria* and (b) *Nereocystis.* Rounded air bladders for flotation are seen in (c) *Sargassum* and other species of brown algae.

a.   b.   c.

green and blue wavelengths of light that penetrate deep into ocean waters. Many red algae also appear green or black or even blue, depending on the depth at which they are growing. Because of this, color is not always a good characteristic to use when determining the classification of algae. **Agar** is a polysaccharide extracted from the cell wall of red algae. Another extract of red algae cell walls, **carrageenan,** is used to give the texture of thickness and richness to foods such as dairy drinks and soups. In Asia and elsewhere, the red algae *Porphyra* (known as *nori*) are used as seaweed wrappers for sushi. The cultivation and production of *Porphyra* constitute a billion-dollar industry.

Procedure

Observe the examples of red algae that are on demonstration.

Results

In Table 3, list the names and characteristics of the red algae on demonstration. Compare the demonstration examples with those illustrated in Figure 5.

Table 3
Representative Red Algae

Name	Body Form (single-celled, filamentous, colonial, leaflike)	Characteristics (reproductive structures, structures for attachment or flotation, pigments)

Discussion

1. What important ecological role is shared by the macroscopic algae (green, red, and brown)?

2. Based on your observations in the laboratory, what two characteristics might you use to distinguish brown and red algae?

a.   b.   c.

Figure 5.

Examples of multicellular red algae (phylum Rhodophyta). (a) Some red algae have deposits of carbonates of calcium and magnesium in their cell walls and are important components of coral reefs. (b) Most red algae have delicate, finely dissected blades. (c) *Porphyra* (or *nori*) is used to make sushi.

Lab Study C. The Green Algae (Chlorophyta)— The Protist-Plant Connection

Materials

cultures or prepared slides of *Spirogyra* sp.
preserved *Ulva lactuca*
preserved *Chara* sp.

Introduction

The green algae include unicellular motile and nonmotile, colonial, filamentous, and multicellular species that inhabit primarily freshwater environments. Because green algae share many characteristics with land plants, including storage of starch and the presence of chlorophylls *a* and *b,* photosynthetic pathways, and organic compounds called flavonoids, most botanists support the hypothesis that plants evolved from green algae. Results of recent work in sequencing ribosomal and transfer RNA genes confirm the close relationship between green algae and land plants, and have led some scientists to propose that green algae, or at least those known as charophytes, be included in the Plant kingdom. In this exercise you will view several body forms of green algae on demonstration: single-celled, filamentous, colonial, and multicellular. Finally, you will observe the multicellular, branched green algae *Chara* (the stonewort), believed to be most similar to the green algae that gave rise to land plants over 460 million years ago.

If you completed the Microscopes and Cells lab, you may remember observing aggregates of single-celled algae, *Protococcus,* and the colonial green algae *Volvox.* In this lab study you will observe the filamentous alga *Spirogyra* sp. and the multicellular algae *Ulva* sp. and *Chara* sp.

Procedure

1. Using your compound microscope, observe living materials or prepared slides of the filamentous alga *Spirogyra* sp. (Figure 6a). This organism is common in small, freshwater ponds. The most obvious structure
   in the cells of the filament is a long chloroplast. Can you determine how
   the alga got its name? Describe the appearance of the chloroplast.

   Can you see a nucleus in each cell of the filament?

2. Observe the preserved specimen of *Ulva* sp., commonly called sea lettuce. This multicellular alga is commonly found on rocks or docks in
   marine and brackish water.

   a. Describe the body form of Ulva.

   b. Are structures present that would serve to attach *Ulva* to its substrate
      (dock or rock)? If so, describe them.

   c. Compare your specimen of *Ulva* with that shown in Figure 6b.

3. Examine the preserved specimen of the multicellular green alga *Chara*.
   This alga grows in muddy or sandy bottoms of clear lakes or ponds. Its
   body form is so complex that it is often mistaken for a plant, but careful study of its structure and reproduction confirms its classification as
   a green alga.

   Note the cylindrical branches attached to nodes. Compare your specimen to Figure 6c. Sketch the appearance of your specimen in the margin of your lab manual.

a.　　　　　　　　　　　　　　　　b.　　　　　　　　　c.

Figure 6.
Examples of multicellular green algae (phylum Chlorophyta). (a) A filamentous green alga, *Spirogyra*. (b) Some green algae are multicellular as in *Ulva*,
sea lettuce. (c) A multicellular, branched green alga, *Chara*.

Results

In Table 4, list the names and characteristics of each green algal species studied. Compare these examples with those illustrated in Figure 6.

Table 4
Representative Green Algae

Name	Body Form (single-celled, filamentous, colonial, leaflike)	Characteristics (pigments, specialized structures, flagella, structures for attachment)
Spirogyra		
Ulva		
Chara		

Lab Study D. Funguslike Protists—Slime Molds (Mycetozoa)

Materials

stereoscopic microscopes
Physarum growing on agar plates

Introduction

The organisms you will investigate in this lab study have been called plants, fungi, animals, fungus animals, protozoa, Protoctista, Protista, Mycetozoa, and probably many more names. William Crowder, in a classic *National Geographic* article (April 1926), describes his search for these creatures in a swamp on the north shore of Long Island. This is what he says: "Behold! Seldom ever before had such a gorgeous sight startled my unexpectant gaze. Spreading out over the bark [of a dead tree] was a rich red coverlet . . . consisting of thousands of small, closely crowded, funguslike growths. . . . A colony of these tiny organisms extended in an irregular patch . . . covering an area nearly a yard in length and slightly less in breadth. . . . Each unit, although actually less than a quarter of an inch in height, resembled . . . a small mushroom, though more marvelous than any I have ever seen."

The creatures Crowder was describing are commonly called **slime molds.** Many place them in the kingdom Fungi, but this classification causes difficulties because, whereas slime molds are phagocytic like protozoa, fungi are never phagocytic but obtain their nutrition by absorption. Characteristics other than feeding mode, including cellular ultrastructure, cell wall chemistry, and molecular studies, indicate that slime molds fit better with amoeboid protists than with fungi. However, the general consensus among taxonomists is that slime molds represent a separate kingdom, the **Mycetozoa** or "fungus-animals."

There are two types of slime molds, plasmodial slime molds and cellular slime molds. In this lab study, you will observe the plasmodial slime mold *Physarum*. The vegetative stage is called a **plasmodium,** and it consists of a multinucleate mass of protoplasm totally devoid of cell walls. This mass feeds on bacteria as it creeps along the surface of moist logs or dead leaves. When conditions are right, it is converted into one or more reproductive structures, called **fruiting bodies,** that produce spores. You may choose to investigate slime molds further in Exercise 3.

Procedure

1. Obtain a petri dish containing *Physarum* and return to your lab bench to study the organism. Keep the dish closed.

2. With the aid of your stereoscopic microscope, examine the plasmodium (Figure 7). Describe characteristics such as color, size, and shape. Look for a system of branching veins. Do you see any movement? Speculate about the source of the movement. Is the movement unidirectional or bidirectional—that is, flows first in one direction and then in the other? Your instructor may have placed oat flakes or another food source on the agar. How does the appearance of the plasmodium change as it contacts a food source?

3. Examine the entire culture for evidence of forming or mature fruiting bodies. Are the fruiting bodies stalked or are they sessile, that is, without a stalk? If a stalk is present, describe it.

Figure 7.
Slime mold. Slime molds are protists that share some characteristics with both protozoa and fungi. The vegetative stage of a plasmodial slime mold includes an amoeboid phase consisting of a multinucleate mass known as a plasmodium.

Results

Sketch the plasmodium and fruiting bodies in the margin of your lab manual. Label structures where appropriate.

Discussion

Slime molds were once placed in the kingdom Fungi. What characteristics suggest that these organisms are protistan?

EXERCISE 2
The Kingdom Fungi

Introduction

The kingdom Fungi includes a diverse group of organisms that play important economic and ecological roles. These organisms are unicellular (yeasts) or multicellular, heterotrophic organisms that obtain their nutrients by absorption, digesting their food outside their bodies and absorbing the digestion products into their cells. They often have complex life cycles with alternating sexual and asexual (vegetative) reproduction. They may produce spores either asexually by mitosis or sexually by meiosis.

Fungi are beneficial to humans in many ways. We have long used fungi to make wine and bake leavened bread. Yeast, a single-celled fungus, is used in the production of wine, beer, and bread; and other fungi are used to produce other foods. *Penicillium* is a fungus that is used to produce antibiotics. In ecosystems, fungi share with bacteria the essential role of decomposition, returning to the ecosystem the matter trapped in dead organisms.

Although many fungi are beneficial, others play destructive roles in nature. Some species parasitize animals and plants. Athlete's foot and ringworm are diseases commonly known to humans, and potato late blight and wheat rust are common plant diseases caused by fungi. The ergot fungus that parasitizes rye causes convulsive ergotism in humans who eat bread made with infested grains. The bizarre behavior of young women who were later convicted of witchcraft in Salem Village, Massachusetts, in 1692 has been attributed to convulsive ergotism. Fungi are also a source of food in many cultures, with truffles being the most expensive. Truffles are dark, edible subterranean fungi that sell for $200 per pound, with an annual harvest of 30 tons. Truffles cannot be grown in a lab or greenhouse, and are located by specially trained truffle-sniffing pigs or dogs.

In this exercise, you will learn about the structure of typical fungi and the characteristics of four important phyla of fungi: Zygomycota, Ascomycota, Basidiomycota, and Deuteromycota. You will see examples of lichens that are associations between fungi and algae. As you observe these examples, consider interesting questions that might be asked about fungi diversity or ecology. You can choose one of these questions to design a simple experiment in Exercise 3.

Lab Study A. Zygote Fungi—Zygomycota

Materials

compound microscope
stereoscopic microscope
cultures of *Rhizopus stolonifer*
   with sporangia
cultures of *Pilobolus crystallinus*
   on demonstration

forceps, ethyl alcohol, alcohol lamp
slides and coverslips
dropper bottles of water

Introduction

One common organism in the phylum Zygomycota is probably growing in your refrigerator right now. The common bread mold, *Rhizopus stolonifer,* grows on many foods as well as bread. In this lab study, you will observe the structure of this species to see many general fungi characteristics. Fungi are made up of threadlike individual filaments, called **hyphae,** which are organized into the body of the fungus, called the **mycelium.** This filamentous mass secretes enzymes into the substrate and digests food that will then be absorbed into its cells. Cells of fungi have cell walls made of **chitin** combined with other complex carbohydrates, including cellulose. You may recall that chitin is the main component of insect exoskeletons.

Rhizopus stolonifer

Rhizopus reproduces both sexually and asexually. In the Zygomycota, cells of the hyphae are haploid. Hyphae grow over a substrate, for example, a slice of bread, giving the bread a fuzzy appearance. In asexual reproduction, certain hyphae grow upright and develop **sporangia,** round structures, on their tips. Haploid spores develop in the sporangia following mitosis, and when they are mature, they are dispersed through the air. If they fall on a suitable medium, they will absorb water and germinate, growing a new mycelium.

Rhizopus also reproduces sexually when compatible mating types designated as (+) and (−) grow side by side. In this case, (+) and (−) hyphae fuse, and, ultimately, nuclei from opposite strains fuse to form $2n$ zygote nuclei that develop in a thick-walled **zygospore.** Following meiosis, haploid spores are produced in sporangia borne on filaments that emerge from the zygospore.

Pilobolus crystallinus

Pilobolus crystallinus (also called the *fungus gun,* or *shotgun fungus*) is another member of the phylum Zygomycota. This fungus is called a **coprophilous** fungus because it grows on dung. It displays many unusual behaviors, one of which is that it is positively phototropic. Perhaps you can investigate this behavior in Exercise 3. Bold et al. (1980) describe asexual reproduction in *Pilobolus.* This species has sporangia as does *Rhizopus,* but rather than similarly dispersing single spores, in *Pilobolus* the sporangium is forcibly discharged as a unit; the dispersion is tied to moisture and diurnal cycles. In nature, in the early evening the sporangia form; shortly after midnight, a swelling appears below the sporangium. Late the following morning, turgor pressure causes the swelling to explode, propelling the sporangium as far as 2 meters. The sticky sporangium will adhere to grass leaves and subsequently may be eaten by an animal—horse, cow, or rabbit. The intact sporangia pass through the animal's digestive tract and are excreted, and the spores germinate in the fresh dung.

In this lab study you will investigate *Rhizopus* and observe *Pilobolus* on demonstration.

Procedure

1. Obtain a culture of *Rhizopus* and carry it to your lab station.
2. Examine it using the stereoscopic microscope.
3. Identify the **mycelia, hyphae,** and **sporangia.**

4. Review the life cycle of *Rhizopus* (Figure 8). Locate the structures in this figure that are visible in your culture. Circle the structures involved in asexual reproduction.

5. Using forceps and aseptic technique, remove a small portion of the mycelium with several sporangia and make a wet mount.

6. Examine the hyphae and sporangia using the compound microscope. Are spores visible? How have the spores been produced?

How do the spores compare with the hyphal cells genetically?

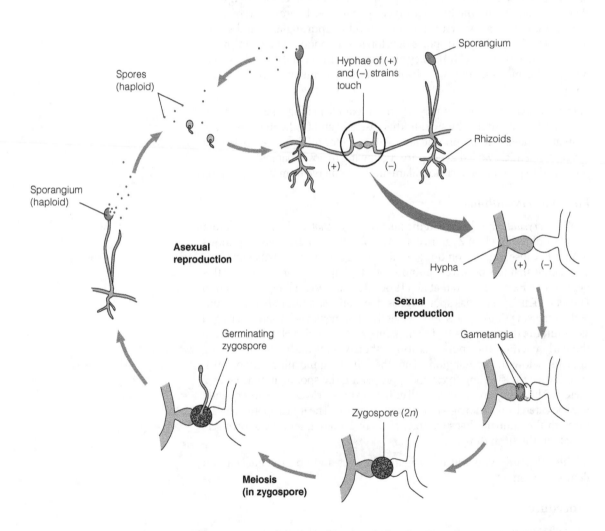

Figure 8.
Rhizopus stolonifer. Rhizopus reproduces both sexually by zygospores and asexually by sporangia producing asexual spores. In sexual reproduction, (+) and (−) mating types fuse and a 2*n* zygospore results.

How would spores produced by sexual reproduction differ from spores produced asexually?

7. Observe the cultures of *Pilobolus* (Figure 9) growing on rabbit dung agar that are on demonstration.

8. Identify the **sporangia, mycelia,** and **hyphae.** What color are the sporangia and spores?

Results

1. Review the life cycle of *Rhizopus* and the structures observed in the living culture and compare with Figure 8.

2. Review the structures observed in *Pilobolus* and compare with Figure 9.

Discussion

1. The body form of most fungi, including *Rhizopus,* is a mycelium composed of filamentous hyphae. Using your observations as a basis for your thinking, state why this body form is well adapted to the fungus mode of nutrition.

2. Refer back to the description of *Pilobolus*. Speculate about the adaptive advantage of having a system to propel sporangia, as seen in *Pilobolus*.

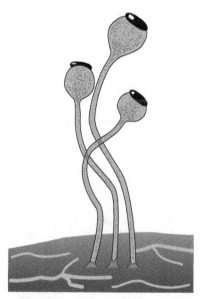

Figure 9.
Pilobolus crystallinus.

Lab Study B. Sac Fungi—Ascomycota

Materials

compound microscope	prepared slide of *Peziza* ascocarp
stereoscopic microscope	preserved or fresh morels
dried or preserved *Peziza* specimen	plastic mounts of ergot in rye or wheat

Introduction

Fungi in the phylum Ascomycota are called *sac fungi,* or ascopore-producing fungi. This division includes edible fungi, morels, and truffles, but it also includes several deadly plant and animal parasites. For example, chestnut blight and the Dutch elm disease have devastated native populations of chestnut and

American elm trees. The fungi causing these diseases were introduced into the United States from Asia and Europe.

Sexual reproduction in the ascomycota fungi produces either four or eight haploid **ascospores** after meiosis in an **ascus.** Spores in *Sordaria* form after meiosis within asci (Figure 7). Asci form within a structure called an **asco-carp.** In *Sordaria* the ascocarp, called a *perithecium,* is a closed, spherical structure that develops a pore at the top for spore dispersal. In some species of sac fungi, the asci are borne on open cup-shaped ascocarps called *apothecia* (sing., *apothecium*). In asexual reproduction, spores are produced, but rather than being enclosed within a sporangium as in zygote fungi, the spores, called **conidia,** are produced on the surface of special reproductive hyphae.

Other features of sac fungi also vary. For example, yeasts are ascomycetes, yet they are single-celled organisms. Yeasts most frequently reproduce asexually by **budding,** a process in which small cells form by pinching off the parent cell. When they reproduce sexually, however, they produce asci, each of which produces four or eight spores.

In this lab study, you will examine a slide of the sac fungi *Peziza* and will observe demonstrations of additional examples of Ascomycota.

Procedure

1. Obtain a dried or preserved specimen of *Peziza* (Figure 10a). Notice the open, cup-shaped apothecium, the **ascocarp,** that bears asci within the cup (not visible with the naked eye). Fungi with ascocarps shaped in this fashion are called **cup fungi.** The cup may be supported by a stalk.

2. Examine a prepared slide of *Peziza* using low and intermediate magnifications on the compound microscope. This slide is a section through the ascocarp. Identify **asci.** How many spores are present per ascus? Are they diploid or haploid?

Figure 10.
Examples of sac fungi, phylum Ascomycota. (a) *Peziza* has a cup-shaped ascocarp with asci within the cup. (b) Morels are cup fungi that resemble mushrooms.

a.

b.

3. Complete the sketch of the ascocarp section below, labeling **asci, spores, hyphae,** and **mycelium**.

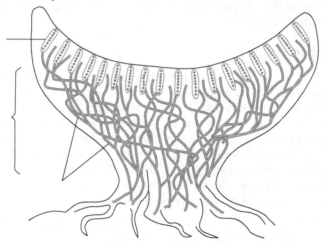

4. Observe the preserved **morels** that are on demonstration (Figure 14.10b). These fungi resemble mushrooms, but the "cap" is convoluted. Asci are located inside the ridges.

5. Observe demonstrations of the mature inflorescence of wheat or rye grass infected with the ascomycete *Claviceps purpurea,* the **ergot** fungus. The large black structures seen among the grains are the ergot.

Results

Review the structures observed in *Peziza*, morels, and ergot. Modify Figures 10a and 10b to reflect features of your examples not included in these figures. Sketch ergot examples in the margin of your lab manual.

Discussion

What characteristics are common to all sac fungi?

Lab Study C. Club Fungi—Basidiomycota

Materials

compound microscope
stereoscopic microscope
fresh, ripe mushroom basidiocarps
prepared slides of *Coprinus* pileus sections

Introduction

The Basidiomycota phylum (club fungi, or basidiospore-producing fungi) includes the fungi that cause the plant diseases wheat rust and corn smut as well as the more familiar puffballs, shelf fungi, and edible and nonedible mushrooms (the latter often called *toadstools*). A mushroom is actually a reproductive structure that grows upward from an underground mycelial mass and produces spores by meiosis. In asexual reproduction, conidia form by mitosis. In this lab study, you will study mushrooms and learn some features of their life cycle.

Procedure

1. Obtain a fresh mushroom, a **basidiocarp,** and identify its parts: The stalk is the **stipe;** the cap is the **pileus.** Look under the cap and identify **gills.** Spores form on the surface of the gills. Examine the gills with the stereoscopic microscope. Do you see spores? Children often make spore prints in scouts or in elementary school by placing a ripe mushroom pileus with the gill side down on a piece of white paper for several hours, allowing the spores to drop to the paper. Scientists use similar spore prints to accurately identify mushrooms.

2. Label the parts of the mushrooms in Figure 11a.

3. Obtain a prepared slide of a section through the pileus of *Coprinus* or another mushroom. Observe it on the compound microscope using low

a.   b.

Figure 11.
Club fungi, phylum Basidiomycota. (a) Mushrooms, or basidiocarps, each consisting of a cap, the pileus; and a stalk, the stipe. (b) A section through the gills on a whole basidiocarp reveals basidia and basidiospores.

and then intermediate powers. Is your slide a cross section or a longitudinal section through the pileus? Make a sketch in the lab manual margin indicating the plane of your section through the basidiocarp. Compare your section with the fresh mushroom you have just studied and with Figure 11b.

4. Using the prepared slide, observe the surface of several gills using high power. Spores are produced at the tips of small club-shaped structures called **basidia.** Locate a basidium and focus carefully on its end. Here you may see four knoblike protuberances. Each protuberance has a haploid nucleus that formed following meiosis, and each becomes a **basidiospore.** When the spores are mature, they are discharged from the basidium and are dispersed by the wind.

Results

Review the structures observed and label Figure 11a. Modify the figure to include features observed in your materials that differ from the figure.

Discussion

State the characteristics shared by all Basidiomycota.

Lab Study D. Imperfect Fungi—Deuteromycota

Materials

cultures of *Penicillium* on demonstration
Roquefort cheese on demonstration

Introduction

Most fungi are classified based on their sexual reproductive structures; however, many fungi (as far as is known) reproduce only vegetatively. Because the sexual reproductive stages of these fungi do not exist or have not been found, they are called **asexual,** or **imperfect fungi** (following the botanical use of "imperfect" to indicate a flower lacking one reproductive part). This group is of interest because several human diseases—athlete's foot, ringworm, and candida "yeast" infections—are caused by species of imperfect fungi. Also in this group are several beneficial species—for example, one species of *Penicillium* that produces the antibiotic penicillin and another that is used to make Roquefort and blue cheeses.

Procedure

1. Observe the *Penicillium* on demonstration. You may have observed something similar growing on oranges or other foods in your refrigerator.
2. Describe the texture and the color of the mycelium.

Results

Sketch your observations of *Penicillium* in the margin of your lab manual. Note any features that may be important in distinguishing this organism.

Discussion

Compare the appearance of *Penicillium* with that of *Rhizopus*.

Lab Study E. Lichens

Materials

examples of foliose, crustose, and fruticose lichens on demonstration

Introduction

Lichens are symbiotic associations between fungi and usually algae or cyanobacteria forming a body that can be consistently recognized. The fungal component is usually a sac fungus or a club fungus. The lichen body, called a **thallus,** varies in shape and colors, depending on the species of the components. Reproductive structures can be bright red or pink or green. Photosynthesis in the algae provides nutrients for the fungus, and the fungus provides a moist environment for the algae or cyanobacterium. Because lichens can survive extremely harsh environments, they are often the first organisms to colonize a newly exposed environment such as volcanic flow or rock outcrops, and they play a role in soil formation.

Procedure

Observe the demonstrations of different lichen types: those with a leafy thallus (**foliose**), a crustlike thallus (**crustose**), or a branching, cylindrical thallus (**fruticose**) (Figure 12). Look for cup-shaped or clublike reproductive structures.

Results

1. Sketch the lichens on demonstration in the margins of your lab manual.
2. Identify and label each according to lichen type.

Discussion

Imagine that you are the first scientist to observe a lichen microscopically. What observations would lead you to conclude that the lichen is composed of a fungus and an alga?

Figure 12.
Lichen types. Lichens may have (a) a leafy thallus (foliose), (b) a crust-like thallus (crustose), or (c) a cylindrical thallus (fruticose).

EXERCISE 3
Designing Your Independent Investigation

Introduction

In this exercise, you will choose one of the organisms observed in this lab topic and design a simple experiment answering a question about its behavior, growth patterns, or interactions with other species.

Be ready to assign tasks to members of your lab team. Be sure that everyone understands the techniques that will be used. Your experiment will be successful only if you plan carefully, cooperate with your team members, perform lab techniques accurately and systematically, and record and report data accurately.

Materials

protozoa and algae cultures
cultures of slime molds *Physarum, Didymium, Dictyostelium*
cultures of *Pilobolus crystallinus, Rhizopus, Penicillium*
sterile agar plates to grow each species
sterile agar with oat flakes
sterile agar with sugar
sterile agar with albumin
sterile agar with pH 6, 7, or 8
aluminum foil
various breads from the health food store—wheat, rye, corn, potato, rice
bread with preservatives
sterilized dung from various animals

Procedure

1. Choose a question from this list to investigate or choose a question from your own observations. *Write your question in the margin of your lab manual.*

   a. Will varying the molarity of the culture medium change the rate of contractile vacuole formation in paramecia?

   b. Do plasmodia of the same species of slime mold unite when growing on the same agar plate? How about different species of slime mold?

   c. Do slime mold plasmodia demonstrate chemotaxis (response to chemical stimuli such as food molecules) or phototaxis (response to light)?

   d. What happens to slime molds if grown in different temperatures?

   e. Do the same fungi grow on different varieties of bread?

   f. How effective are preservatives in preventing fungal growth on foods?

   g. Is *Pilobolus* phototaxic? What about other fungi?

   h. Does succession take place in dung cultures of fungi?

2. Formulate a testable hypothesis.

   Hypothesis:

3. Summarize the experiment. (Use separate paper.)

4. Predict the results of your experiment based on your hypothesis.

   Prediction: (If/then)

5. Outline the procedures used in the experiment.

a. On a separate sheet of paper, list in numerical order each exact step of your procedure.

b. Remember to include the number of replicates (usually a minimum of five), levels of treatment, appropriate time intervals, and controls for each procedure.

c. If you have an idea for an experiment that requires materials other than those provided, ask your laboratory instructor about availability. If possible, additional supplies will be provided.

d. When carrying out an experiment, remember to quantify your measurements when possible.

6. Perform the experiment, making observations and collecting data for analysis.

7. **Record observations and data** on a separate sheet of paper. Design tables and graphs, at least one of each. Be thorough when collecting data. Do not just write down numbers, but record what they mean as well. Do not rely on your memory for information that you will need when reporting your results.

8. **Prepare your discussion.** Discuss your results in light of your hypothesis.

a. Review your hypothesis. Review your results (tables and graphs). Do your results support of falsify your hypothesis? Explain your answer, using data for support.

b. Review your prediction. Did your results correspond to the prediction you made? If not, explain how your results are different from your predictions, and why this might have occurred.

c. If you had problems with the procedure or questionable results, explain how they might have influenced your conclusion.

d. If you had an opportunity to repeat and expand this experiment to make your results more convincing, what would you do?

e. Summarize the conclusion you have drawn from your results.

9. **Be prepared to report your results to the class.** Prepare to persuade your fellow scientists that your experimental design is sound and that your results support your conclusions.

10. If your instructor requires it, **submit a written laboratory report** in the form of a scientific paper. Keep in mind that although you have performed the experiments as a team, you must turn in a lab report of *your original writing*. Your tables and figures may be similar to those of your team members, but your paper must be the product of your own literature search and creative thinking.

Questions for Review

1. Complete Table 5 comparing charactistics of algae.
2. Complete Table 6 comparing characteristics of fungi.

Table 5
Comparison of Algae by Major Features

Phylum	Example(s)	Characteristics	Ecological Role	Economic Importance
Dinoflagellata				
Bacillariophyta				
Phaeophyta (Brown Algae)				
Rhodophyta (Red Algae)				
Chlorophyta (Green Algae)				

3. Compare spore formation in sac fungi and club fungi.

Table 6

Comparison of Fungi by Major Features

Phylum	Example(s)	Sexual Reproductive Structures	Asexual Reproductive Structures
Zygomycota (Zygote Fungi)			
Ascomycota (Sac Fungi)			
Basidiomycota (Club Fungi)			
Deuteromycota (Imperfect Fungi)			

4. Using observations of pigments present, body form, and distinguishing characteristics of the three groups of macroscopic green, brown, and red algae, speculate about where they might be most commonly found in ocean waters.

Applying Your Knowledge

1. Scientists are concerned that the depletion of the ozone layer will result in a reduction of populations of marine algae such as diatoms and

dinoflagellates. Recall the ecological role of these organisms and comment on the validity of this concern.

2. Imagine an ecosystem with no fungi. How would it be modified?

3. In 1950 the living world was classified simply into two kingdoms: plants and animals. More recently, scientists developed the five-kingdom system of classification: plants, animals, monerans, protists, and fungi. In 2000 there was a general consensus among scientists that three domains with more than five kingdoms was a better system for classifying the diversity of life on Earth. However, there is still no consensus on the number of kingdoms or the clustering of organisms that best represents their evolutionary relationships. Using the protists studied in this lab topic, explain why the classification of this diverse group in particular is problematic. How is solving the problem of organizing protistan diversity a model for understanding the process of science?

References

Ahmadjian, V. "Lichens Are More Important Than You Think," *BioScience,* 1995, vol. 45, p. 124.

Alexopoulos, C., C. Mims, and M. Blackwell. *Introductory Mycology,* 4th ed. New York, NY: John Wiley and Sons, Inc., 1996.

Anderson, R. "What to Do with Protists?" *Australian Systematic Botany,* 1998, vol. 11, p. 185.

Bold, H., C. J. Alexopoulos, and T. Delevoryas. *Morphology of Plants and Fungi.* New York: Harper & Row, 1980, p. 654.

Campbell, N., and J. Reece. *Biology,* 6th ed. Menlo Park, CA: Benjamin/Cummings, 2002.

Crowder, W. "Marvels of Mycetozoa." *National Geographic Magazine,* 1926, vol. 49, pp. 421–443.

Doolittle, W. F. "Uprooting the Tree of Life," *Scientific American,* 2000, vol. 282, pp. 90–95.

Hickman, C. P., L. S. Roberts, and A. Larson. *Integrated Principles of Zoology,* 11th ed. Boston: McGraw-Hill, 2001.

Litten, W. "The Most Poisonous Mushrooms," *Scientific American,* 1975, vol. 232.

Websites

Excellent site discussing Protistan systematics:
http://www.ucmp.berkeley.edu/alllife/eukaryotasy.html

Protist Image Data. Excellent page links:
http://megasun.bch.umontreal.ca/protists/protists.html

Links to pictures of red, brown, and green algae:
http://www.sonoma.edu/biology/algae/algae.html

Seaweeds:
http://www.botany.uwc.ac.za/Envfacts/seaweeds/

Information about specific algae and other interesting links:

http://www.botany.uwc.ac.za/mirrors/UCG_Seawwwd/Algae/

Mycological Resources on the Internet:

http://muse/bio.cornell.edu/~fungi/

See an amoeba video and find interesting information on amoebas:

http://www.bms.ed.ac.uk/research/smaciver/amoeba.htm

Photo Credits

1b: ©Biophoto Associates/Science Source/Photo Researchers, Inc. 2b: Courtesy of John Mansfield, University of Wisconsin, Madison. 3a: Courtesy of the Virginia Institute of Marine Science/William and Mary. 3b: Courtesy of Jean-Marie CAVANIHAC/Jean-Marie CAVANIHAC. 3c: Courtesy of JoAnn Burkholder, North Carolina State University. 3d: ©Eric Grave/Photo Researchers, Inc. 3c: ©Michael Abbey/Photo Researchers, Inc. 3d: ©Cabisco/Visuals Unlimited. 5a: ©Gary Robinson/Visuals Unlimited. 5b: ©D. P. Wilson/Eric and David Hosking/Photo Researchers, Inc. 5c: Courtesy of Wayne Armstrong/Wayne's World. 6a: ©Kim Taylor/Bruce Coleman, Inc. 6c: ©Kerry A. Dressler/Biological Photo Service. 7: ©R. R. Degginger/Earth Scenes/Animals Animals.

Art Credits

6c: From Bold et al., *Morphology of Plants and Fungi,* 5th ed. (New York: Harper and Row, 1987), ©1987 by Harper and Row Publishers, Inc. Reprinted by permission of Addison Wesley Longman, Inc. 9, 10: Adapted from illustrations by Miguel Ulloa, Departamento de Botanica, Instituto de Biologia, Universidad Nacional Autonoma de Mexico. 11, 12: ©Miguel Ulloa.

Text Credits

Excerpt from William Crowder, "Marvels of Mycetozoa," *National Geographic Magazine,* April 1926. Copyright ©1926 National Geographic Society. Reprinted by permission.

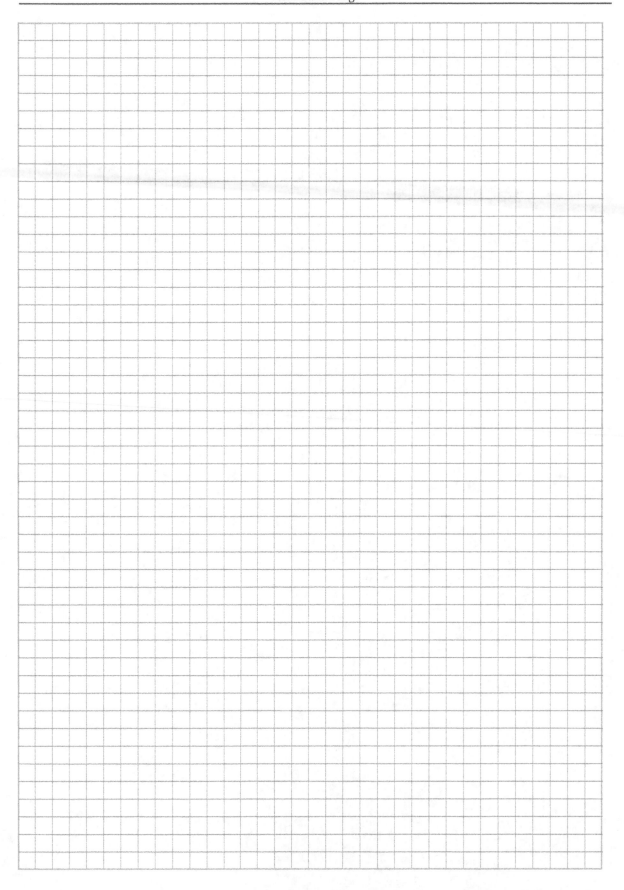

Plant Diversity I:
Bryophytes and Seedless Vascular Plants

Laboratory Objectives

After completing this lab topic, you should be able to:

1. Describe the distinguishing characteristics of bryophytes and seedless vascular plants.

2. Discuss the primitive and advanced features of bryophytes and seedless vascular plants relative to their adaptations to the land environment.

3. Recognize and identify representative members of each division of bryophytes and seedless vascular plants.

4. Describe in detail the life cycle of a moss and a fern, including the important structures and processes in each life cycle.

5. Identify fossil members and their extant counterparts in the seedless vascular plants.

6. Describe the general life cycle and alternation of generations in the bryophytes and the seedless vascular plants, and discuss the differences between the life cycles of the two groups of plants using examples.

7. Describe homospory and heterospory, including the differences in spores and gametophytes.

8. Discuss the ecological role and economic importance of these groups of plants.

Introduction

In the history of life on Earth, one of the most revolutionary events was the colonization of land, first by plants, then by animals. Evidence from comparisons of extant land plants and divisions of algae suggests that the first land plants were related to the green algae. These first colonists are thought to be most similar to the living, branched, multicellular green alga *Chara*. Once these primitive plants arrived on land over 500 million years ago, they faced new and extreme challenges in their physical environment. Only individuals that were able to survive the variations in temperature, moisture, gravitational forces, and substrate would thrive. Out of this enormous selective regime would come new and different adaptations and new and different life forms: the land plants.

Land plants generally have complex, multicellular plant bodies that are specialized for a variety of functions. Specialized structures have evolved for protection of the vulnerable stages of sexual reproduction. The plant body is often covered with a waxy cuticle that prevents desiccation. However, the waxy covering also prevents gas exchange, a problem solved by the presence of openings called **stomata** (sing., **stoma**). Some land plants have developed vascular tissue for efficient movement of materials throughout these

From *Investigating Biology,* Fourth Edition, Judith Giles Morgan and M. Eloise Brown Carter. Copyright © 2002 Pearson Education, Inc., publishing as Benjamin Cummings. All rights reserved.

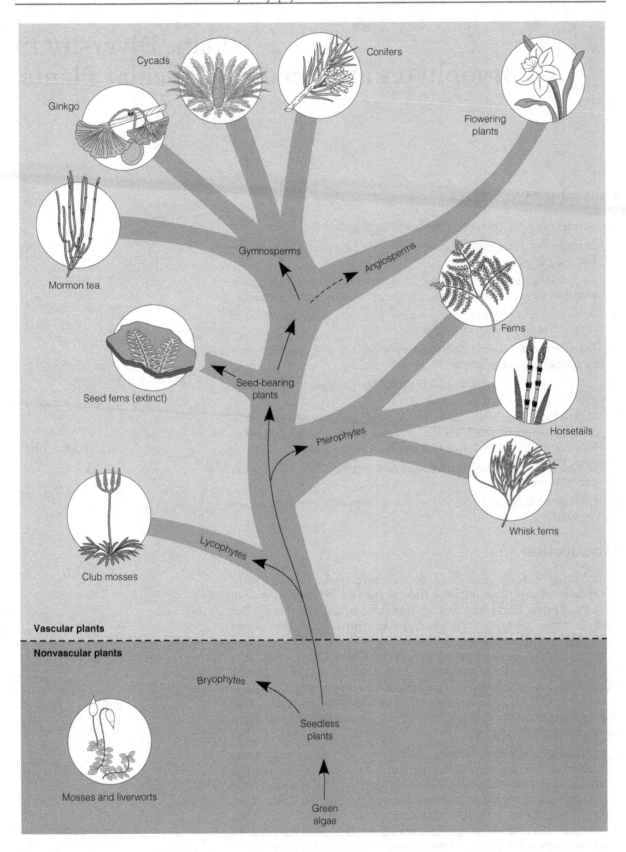

Table 1
Classification of Land Plants

Classification	Common Name	Illustration
Nonvascular Plants		
Division Bryophyta	Mosses	
Division Hepatophyta	Liverworts	
Division Anthocerophyta	Hornworts	
Vascular Plants		
Seedless Plants		
Division Lycophyta	Club mosses	
Division Pterophyta	Ferns, horsetails, whisk ferns	
Seed Plants		
Gymnosperms		
Division Coniferophyta	Conifers	
Division Cycadophyta	Cycads	
Division Ginkgophyta	Ginkgo	
Division Gnetophyta	Gnetae	
Angiosperms		
Division Anthophyta	Flowering plants	

complex bodies, which are no longer bathed in water. As described in the following section, the reproductive cycles and reproductive structures of these plants are also adapted to the land environment.

In the two plant diversity labs, you will be investigating the diversity of land plants (Table 1 and Figure 1), some of which will be familiar to you (flowering plants, pine trees, and ferns) and some of which you may never have seen before (whisk ferns, horsetails, and liverworts). Remember as you view the classification that the designations *phylum* and *division* are equivalent taxonomic groupings. Botanists traditionally use division. You will study the bryophytes and seedless vascular plants in this lab topic, Plant Diversity I. *To maintain your perspective in the face of all this diversity—and to remember the major themes of these labs—bear in mind the questions that follow.*

(✎) **Figure 1.**
Evolution of land plants. The bryophytes and vascular plants probably evolved from green algae over 460 million years ago. Seedless vascular plants dominated Earth 300 million years ago, and representatives of four divisions have survived until the present. Seed plants replaced the seedless plants, and today flowering plants are the most diverse and successful group in an amazing variety of habitats. The representatives studied in Plant Diversity I and II are indicated.

1. What are the special adaptations of these plants to the land environment?
2. How are specialized plant structures related to functions in the land environment?
3. What are the major trends in the plant kingdom as plant life evolved over the past 500 million years?
4. In particular, how has the fundamental reproductive cycle of alternation of generations been modified in successive groups of plants?

Plant Life Cycles

All land plants have a common sexual reproductive life cycle called **alternation of generations,** in which plants alternate between a haploid **gametophyte** generation and a diploid **sporophyte** generation (Figure 2). In living land plants, these two generations differ in their morphology. In all land plants except the bryophytes (mosses and liverworts), the diploid sporophyte generation is the dominant (more conspicuous) generation. The sporophyte generation undergoes meiosis to produce haploid **spores** in a protective, nonreproductive jacket of cells called the **sporangium.** The spores germinate to produce the haploid gametophyte, which produces **gametes** inside a jacket of cells forming **gametangia** (sing., **gametangium**). **Eggs** are produced in **archegonia** (sing., **archegonium**), and **sperm** are produced in **antheridia** (sing., **antheridium**). These haploid gametes are formed by mitosis. The gametes fuse, usually by the entrance of the sperm into the archegonium, forming a diploid **zygote,** the first stage of the diploid sporophyte generation.

Note that both gametes and spores are haploid in this life cycle. Unlike the animal life cycle, however, *the plant life cycle produces gametes by mitosis; spores are produced by meiosis.* The difference between these two cells is that

Figure 2.
Alternation of generations. In this life cycle, a diploid sporophyte plant alternates with a haploid gametophyte plant. Note that haploid spores are produced on the sporophyte by meiosis, and haploid gametes are produced in the gametophyte by mitosis. *Using a colored pencil, indicate the structures that are haploid, and with another color, note the structures that are diploid.*

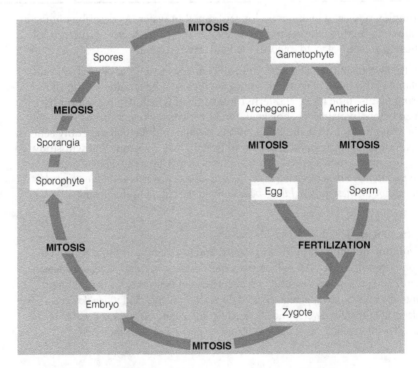

gametes fuse with other gametes to form the zygote and restore the diploid number, while spores germinate to form a new haploid gametophyte plant.

Review the generalized diagram of this life cycle in Figure 2. *Using colored pencils, note the structures that are diploid and those that are haploid.* As you become familiar with variations of this life cycle through specific examples, you will want to continue referring to this general model for review.

Major trends in the evolution of this life cycle include the increased importance of the sporophyte as the photosynthetic and persistent plant that dominates the life cycle; the reduction and protection of the gametophyte within the body of the sporophyte; and the evolution of seeds and then flowers.

Bryophytes and Seedless Vascular Plants

In this lab topic, terrestrial plants will be used to illustrate how life has undergone dramatic changes during the past 500 million years. Not long after the transition to land, plants diverged into at least two separate lineages. One gave rise to the bryophytes, a group of mostly nonvascular plants, including the mosses, and the other to the vascular plants (see Figure 1). Bryophytes first appear in the fossil record dating over 400 million years ago and remain unchanged, whereas the vascular plants have undergone enormous diversification. As you review the evolution of land plants, refer to the geological time chart for an overview of the history of life on Earth (Figure 3, on the next page).

EXERCISE 1

Bryophytes

The bryophytes are composed of three divisions of related plants that share some key characteristics and include mosses (Bryophyta) and liverworts (Hepatophyta). The third division, hornworts (Anthocerophyta), will not be seen in lab. (See again Figure 1 and Table 1.) The term *bryophytes* does not refer to a taxonomic category; rather, bryophytes are an ancient group of plants that appear to have evolved into several different groups independently and did not give rise to any other living groups of plants. They are small plants generally lacking **vascular tissue** (specialized cells for the transport of material), although water-conducting tubes appear to be present in some mosses. (However, these tubes may be unrelated to the vascular tissue in vascular plants.) The life cycle for the bryophytes differs from all other land plants because the gametophyte is the dominant and conspicuous plant. Because bryophytes are nonvascular, they are restricted to moist habitats and have never attained the size and importance of other groups of plants. The gametophyte plants remain close to the ground, enabling the motile sperm to swim from the antheridium to the archegonium and fertilize the egg. They have a cuticle but lack stomata on the surface of the **thallus** (plant body), which is not organized into roots, stems, and leaves.

Years Ago (millions)	Era Period Epoch	Life on Earth
	CENOZOIC Quaternary	
	Recent Pleistocene	• Origin of agriculture and artificial selection; *H. sapiens*
— 1.8 —	Tertiary	
	Pliocene	• Large carnivores; hominoid apes
— 5 —	Miocene	• Forests dwindle; grassland spreads
— 23 —	Oligocene	• Anthropoid apes
— 35 —	Eocene	• Diversification of mammals and flowering plants
— 57 —	Paleocene	• Specialized flowers; sophisticated pollinators and seed distributors
— 65 —	**MESOZOIC**	
	Cretaceous	• Flowering plants established and diversified; many modern families present; extinction of many dinosaurs
— 145 —	Jurassic	• Origin of birds; reptiles dominant; cycads and ferns abundant; first modern conifers and immediate ancestors of flowering plants
— 208 —	Triassic	• First dinosaurs and mammals; forests of gymnosperms and ferns; cycads
— 245 —	**PALEOZOIC**	
	Permian	• Diversification of gymnosperms; origin of reptiles; amphibians dominant
— 290 —	Carboniferous	• First treelike plants; giant woody lycopods and sphenopsids form extensive forests in swampy areas; evolution of early seeds (seed ferns) and first stages of leaves
— 363 —	Devonian	• Diversification of vascular plants; sharks and fishes dominant in the oceans
— 409 —	Silurian	• First vascular plants
— 439 —	Ordovician	• Diversification of algae and plants invade land
— 510 —	Cambrian	• Diversification of major animal phyla
— 570 —	**PRECAMBRIAN**	
	Precambrian	• Origin of bacteria, archaea, and eukaryotes
Earth is about 4.6 billion years old		

Bryophytes are not important economically, with the exception of sphagnum moss, which in its harvested and dried form is known as *peat moss.* Peat moss is absorbent, has an antibacterial agent, and was reportedly once used as bandages and diapers. Today peat moss is used primarily in the horticultural industry.

Lab Study A. Bryophyta: Mosses

Materials

living examples of mosses
prepared slides of *Mnium* archegonia and antheridia
colored pencils

Introduction

The mosses are the most common group of bryophytes, occurring primarily in moist environments but also found in dry habitats that are periodically wet. Refer to Figure 4 on the next page as you investigate the moss life cycle, which is representative of the bryophytes.

Procedure

1. Examine living colonies of mosses on demonstration. Usually you will find the two generations, gametophyte and sporophyte, growing together.

2. Identify the leafy **gametophytes** and the dependent **sporophytes,** which appear as elongated structures growing above them. Tug gently at the sporophyte and notice that it is attached to the gametophyte. Recall that the sporophyte develops and matures while attached to the gametophyte and receives its moisture and nutrients from the gametophyte.

3. The gametes are produced by the gametophyte in **gametangia,** which protect the gametes but are not readily visible without a microscope. Observe under the microscope's low-power lens prepared slides containing long sections of heads of the unisex moss *Mnium,* which contain the gametangia. One slide has been selected to show the **antheridia** (male); the other is a rosette of **archegonia** (female). Sperm-forming tissue will be visible inside the antheridia. On the archegonial slide, look for an archegonium. The moss archegonium has a very long neck and rounded base. It will be difficult to find an entire archegonium in any one section. Search for a single-celled **egg** in the base of the archegonium.

4. Refer to Figure 4 as you follow the steps of fertilization through formation of the gametophyte in the next generation. The sperm swim

(✇) **Figure 3.**
Geological time chart. The history of life can be organized into time periods that reflect changes in the physical and biological environment. Refer to this table as you review the evolution of land plants in Plant Diversity I and II.

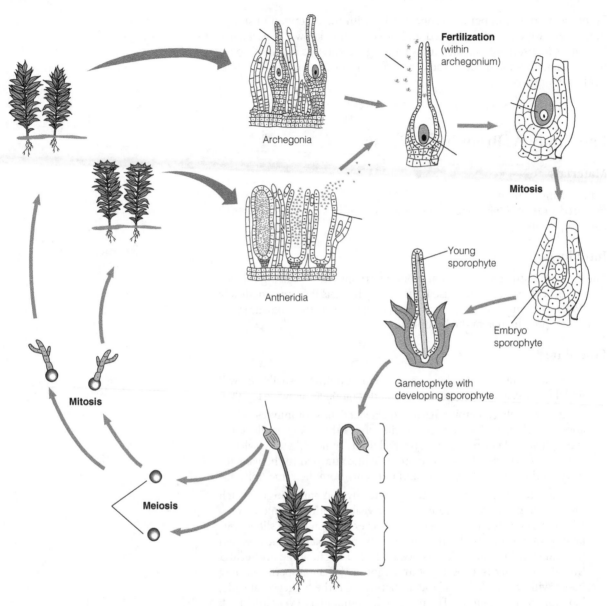

Fertilization
(within
archegonium)

Archegonia

Mitosis

Antheridia

Young
sporophyte

Embryo
sporophyte

Gametophyte with
developing sporophyte

Mitosis

Meiosis

Figure 4.
Moss life cycle. The leafy moss plant is the gametophyte, and the sporophyte is dependent on it, deriving its water and nutrients from the body of the gametophyte. Review this variation of alternation of generations and label the structures described in Lab Study A. *Using colored pencils, highlight the haploid and diploid structures in different colors. Circle the processes of mitosis and meiosis.*

through a film of water to the archegonium and swim down the neck to the egg, where fertilization takes place. The diploid zygote divides by mitosis and develops into an embryonic sporophyte within the archegonium. As the sporophyte matures, it grows out of the gametophyte but remains attached, deriving water and nutrients from the gametophyte body. **Spores** develop in the **sporangium** at the end of the sporophyte. The spores are discharged from the sporangium and in a favorable environment develop into new gametophytes.

Results

1. Review the structures and processes observed and then label the moss life cycle diagram in Figure 4.
2. Using colored pencils, indicate if structures are haploid or diploid and circle the processes of mitosis and meiosis.

Discussion

Refer to Figure 2, the generalized diagram of the plant life cycle.

1. Are the spores produced by the moss sporophyte formed by meiosis or mitosis? Are they haploid or diploid?

2. Do the spores belong to the gametophyte or sporophyte generation?

3. Are the gametes haploid or diploid? Are they produced by meiosis or mitosis?

4. Is the dominant generation for the bryophytes the gametophyte or the sporophyte?

5. Can you suggest any ecological role for bryophytes?

6. What feature of the life cycle differs for bryophytes compared with all other land plants?

Lab Study B. Hepatophyta: Liverworts

Materials

living liverworts

Introduction

Liverworts are so named because their bodies are flattened and lobed. Early herbalists believed that these plants were beneficial in the treatment of liver disorders. Although less common than mosses, liverworts can be found along streams on moist rocks, but because of their small size, you must look closely to locate them.

Procedure

Examine examples of liverworts on demonstration. Liverworts have a flat **thallus** (plant body). Note the **rhizoids,** rootlike extensions on the lower surface. Observe the **pores** on the surface of the leaflike thallus. These openings function in gas exchange; however, they are always open since they lack guard cells. On the upper surface of the thallus you should see circular cups called **gemmae cups,** which contain flat disks of green tissue called **gemmae.** The gemmae are washed out of the cups when it rains, and they grow into new, genetically identical liverworts.

Results

Sketch the overall structure of the liverwort in the margin of your laboratory manual. Label structures where appropriate.

Discussion

1. Is the plant you observed the gametophyte or sporophyte?

2. Are the gemmae responsible for asexual or sexual reproduction? Explain.

3. Why are these plants, like most bryophytes, restricted to moist habitats, and why are they always small?

4. In this lab topic, you are asked to complete tables that summarize features advantageous to the adaptation of plant groups to the land environment. You may be asked to compare these derived (advanced) features with others that have changed little (primitive) in the evolution of land plants. For example, for bryophytes, motile sperm might be considered a primitive feature, while the cuticle would be considered advanced.

   Complete Table 2, relating the features of bryophytes to their success in the land environment. Refer to the lab topic introduction for assistance.

48

Table 2
Primitive and Advanced Features of Bryophytes as
They Relate to Adaptation to Land

Primitive Features	Advanced Features

EXERCISE 2
Seedless Vascular Plants

Seedless, terrestrial plants are analogous to the first terrestrial vertebrate animals, the amphibians, in their dependence on water for external fertilization and development of the unprotected, free-living embryo. Both groups were important in the Paleozoic era but have undergone a steady decline in importance since that time. Seedless plants were well suited for life in the vast swampy areas that covered large areas of the Earth in the Carboniferous period but were not suited for the drier areas of the Earth at that time or for later climatic changes that caused the vast swamps to decline and disappear. The fossilized remains of the swamp forests are the coal deposits of today (Figure 3).

Although living representatives of the seedless vascular plants have survived for millions of years, their limited adaptations to the land environment have restricted their range. All seedless vascular plants have vascular tissue, which is specialized for conducting water, nutrients, and photosynthetic products. Their life cycle is a variation of alternation of generations, in which the sporophyte is the dominant plant; the gametophyte is usually independent of the sporophyte. These plants have stomata and structural support tissue. However, since they still retain the primitive feature of motile sperm that require water for fertilization, the gametophyte is small and restricted to moist habitats.

Economically, the only important members of this group are the ferns, a significant horticultural resource.

The divisions included in the seedless vascular plants are Lycophyta and Pterophyta (see again Table 1 and Figure 1).

Lab Study A. Lycophyta: Club Mosses

Materials

living *Selaginella* and *Lycopodium*
preserved *Selaginella* with microsporangia and megasporangia
prepared slide of *Selaginella* strobilus, l.s.

Introduction

Living members of Lycophyta are usually found in moist habitats, including bogs and streamsides. However, one species of *Selaginella*, the resurrection plant, inhabits deserts. It remains dormant throughout periods of low rainfall, but then comes to life—resurrects—when it rains. During the Carboniferous period, lycophytes were not inconspicuous parts of the flora but rather formed the forest canopy; they were the ecological equivalent of today's oaks, hickories, and pines.

Bryophytes and most seedless vascular plants produce one type of spore (**homospory**), which gives rise to the gametophyte by mitosis. One advanced feature occasionally seen in seedless vascular plants is the production of two kinds of spores (**heterospory**). Large spores called **megaspores** divide by mitosis to produce the female gametophyte. The numerous small spores, **microspores,** produce the male gametophytes by mitosis. Heterospory and separate male and female gametophytes, as seen in *Selaginella*, are unusual in seedless vascular plants, but characteristic of seed-producing vascular plants.

Procedure

1. Examine living club mosses, *Selaginella* and *Lycopodium*. Are they dichotomously branched? (The branches would split in two, appearing to form a Y.) Locate sporangia, which may be present either clustered at the end of the leafy stem tips, forming **strobili**, or **cones**, or dispersed along the leafy stems. Note that these plants have small leaves, or bracts, along the stem.

2. Examine preserved strobili of *Selaginella*. Observe the round sporangia clustered in sporophylls (leaflike structures) at the tip of the stem. These sporangia contain either four megaspores or numerous microspores. Can you observe any differences in the sporangia or spores?

3. Observe the prepared slide of a long section through the strobilus of *Selaginella*. Begin your observations at low power. Are both microspores and megaspores visible on this slide?

   How can you distinguish these spores?

4. Identify the **strobilus, microsporangium, microspores, megasporangium,** and **megaspores** and label Figure 5.

50

a. Mature sporophyte (2*n*)

b.

Figure 5.
Selaginella. (a) The leafy plant is the sporophyte. The sporangia are clustered at the tips in strobili. (b) Photomicrograph of a longitudinal section through the strobilus of *Selaginella.*

Results

1. Sketch the overall structure of the club mosses in the margin of your lab manual. Label structures where appropriate.
2. Review Figure 5 of *Selaginella*. Using a colored pencil, highlight the structures that are haploid and part of the gametophyte generation.

Discussion

1. Are these leafy plants part of the sporophyte or the gametophyte generation? Do you have any evidence to support your answer?

2. What features would you look for to determine if this were a seedless vascular plant?

3. Are microspores and megaspores produced by mitosis or meiosis? (Review the life cycle in Figure 2.)

4. Will megaspores divide to form the female gametophyte or the sporophyte?

 Having trouble with life cycles? Return to the introduction and review the generalized life cycle in Figure 2. Reread the introduction to the study of seedless vascular plants. The key to success is to determine where meiosis occurs and to remember the ploidal level for the gametophyte and the sporophyte.

Lab Study B. Pterophyta: Ferns, Horsetails, and Whisk Ferns

Materials

living and/or preserved horsetails (*Equisetum*)
living and/or preserved whisk ferns (*Psilotum*)
living ferns

Introduction

If a time machine could take us back 400 million years to the Silurian period, we would find that vertebrate animals were confined to the seas, and early vascular plants had begun to diversify on land (Table 3). By the Carboniferous period, ferns, horsetails, and whisk ferns grew alongside the lycophytes. Until recently, these three groups of seedless vascular plants were placed in separate divisions: Pterophyta (ferns), Sphenophyta (horsetails), and Psilophyta (whisk ferns). Strong evidence from molecular biology now reveals a close relationship among these three groups, supporting a common ancestor for the group and their placement in one division, Pterophyta.

Psilophytes (**whisk ferns**) are diminutive, dichotomously branched (repeated Y branches), photosynthetic stems that reproduce sexually by aerial spores. Today, whisk ferns can be found in some areas of Florida and in the tropics. Sphenophytes (**horsetails**) have green jointed stems with occasional clusters of leaves or branches. Their cell walls contain silica that give the stem a rough texture. These plants were used by pioneers to scrub dishes—thus their name, scouring rushes. In cooler regions of North America, horsetails grow as weeds along roadsides. **Ferns** are the most successful group of seedless vascular plants, occupying habitats from the desert to tropical rain forests. Most ferns are small plants that lack woody tissue. An exception is the tree ferns found in tropical regions. Many cultivated ferns are available for home gardeners.

In this lab study you will investigate the diversity of pterophytes, including whisk ferns, horsetails, and a variety of ferns. The plants on demonstration are sporophytes, the dominant generation in seedless vascular plants. You will investigate the life cycle of a fern in Lab Study C, Fern Life Cycle.

Procedure

1. Examine a living **whisk fern** (*Psilotum nudum*) on demonstration. This is one of only two extant genera of psilophytes.

2. Observe the spherical structures on the stem. If possible, cut one open and determine the function of these structures. Note the dichotomous branching, typical of the earliest land plants.

3. Examine the **horsetails** (*Equisetum* sp.) on demonstration. Note the ribs and ridges in the stem. Also examine the nodes or joints along the stem where branches and leaves may occur in some species. Locate the **strobili** in the living or preserved specimens on demonstration. These are clusters of **sporangia**, which produce **spores.**

4. Examine the living **ferns** on demonstration. Note the deeply dissected leaves, which arise from an underground stem called a **rhizome,** which functions like a root to anchor the plant. Roots arise from the rhizome. Observe the dark spots, or **sori** (sing. **sorus**), which are clusters of sporangia, on the underside of some leaves, called **sporophylls**.

Results

1. Sketch the overall structure of the whisk fern, horsetail, and fern in the margin of your lab manual. Label structures where appropriate.

2. Are there any leaves on the whisk fern? On the horsetails?

3. Are sporangia present on the whisk fern? On the horsetails? On the ferns?

Discussion

1. Are the spores in the sporangia produced by mitosis or meiosis?

2. Are the sporangia haploid or diploid? Think about which generation produces them.

3. Once dispersed, will these spores produce the gametophyte or sporophyte generation?

Lab Study C. Fern Life Cycle

Materials

living ferns	stereoscopic microscope
living fern gametophytes with archegonia and antheridia	compound microscope prepared slide of fern gametophytes with archegonia, c.s.
living fern gametophytes with young sporophytes attached	colored pencils Protoslo®

Introduction

In the previous Lab Study you examined the features of the fern sporophyte. In this lab study you will examine the fern life cycle in more detail, beginning with the sporophyte.

Procedure

1. Examine the sporophyte leaf with sori at your lab bench. Make a water mount of a sorus and examine the sporangia using a dissecting microscope. You will find the stalked **sporangia** in various stages of development. Find a sporangium still filled with **spores** and another that has discharged its spores. The sporangia contain cells in different stages of meiosis, leading to spores that are seen in different stages of maturation. These stages will not be distinguishable to you under the microscope.

2. Refer to Figure 6 as you observe the events and important structures in the life cycle of the fern. The haploid spores of ferns fall to the ground and grow into heart-shaped, **gametophyte** plants. All seedless terrestrial plants depend on an external source of water for a sperm to swim to an egg to effect fertilization and for growth of the resulting sporophyte plant. The sexual organs, which bear male and female gametes, are borne on the underside of the gametophyte. Egg cells are borne in urn-like structures called **archegonia,** and sperm cells are produced in globular structures called **antheridia.** Archegonia are usually found around the notch of the heart-shaped gametophyte, while antheridia occur over most of the undersurface.

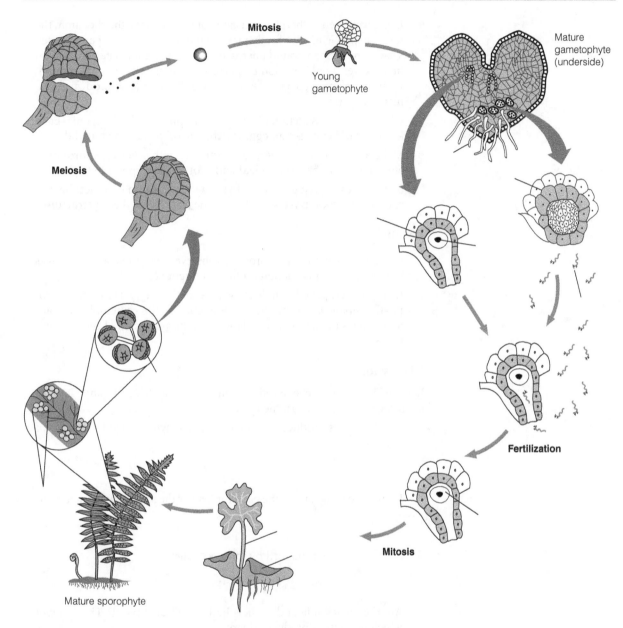

Figure 6.
Fern life cycle. The familiar leafy fern plant is the sporophyte, which alternates with a small, heart-shaped gametophyte. Review this life cycle, a variation of alternation of generations, and label the structures and processes described in Lab Study C. *Using colored pencils, highlight the haploid and diploid structures in different colors.*

3. To study whole gametophytes, make a slide of living gametophytes. View them using the stereoscopic microscope or the scanning lens on the compound microscope. Note their shape and color and the presence of **rhizoids,** rootlike multicellular structures. Locate archegonia and antheridia. Which surface will you need to examine? Sketch in the margin of your lab manual any details not included in Figure 6.

4. If you have seen antheridia on a gametophyte, remove the slide from the microscope. Gently but firmly press on the coverslip with a pencil eraser. View using the compound microscope first on intermediate and then on high power. Look for motile **sperm** swimming with a spiral motion. Each sperm has two flagella. Add a drop of Protoslo to slow down movement of sperm.

5. Observe the cross section of a fern gametophyte with archegonia. Each archegonium encloses an **egg,** which may be visible on your slide.

6. Make a wet mount of a fern gametophyte with a **young sporophyte** attached. Look for a young **leaf** and **root** on each sporophyte.

    Share slides of living gametophytes with archegonia, antheridia and sperm, and sporophytes until everyone has observed each structure.

Results

1. Review the structures and processes observed, and then label the stages of fern sexual reproduction outlined in Figure 6.

2. Using colored pencils, circle those parts of the life cycle that are sporophytic (diploid). Use another color to encircle the gametophytic (haploid) stages of the life cycle. Highlight the processes of meiosis and mitosis.

Discussion

Refer to Figure 2, the generalized diagram of the plant life cycle, and Figure 6, a representation of the fern life cycle.

1. Are the spores produced by the fern sporophyte formed by meiosis or mitosis?

2. Do the spores belong to the gametophyte or the sporophyte generation?

3. Are the gametes produced by mitosis or meiosis?

4. Are the archegonia and antheridia haploid or diploid? Think about which generation produces them.

5. Is the dominant generation for the fern the gametophyte or the sporophyte?

6. Can you suggest any ecological role for ferns?

Lab Study D. Fossils of Seedless Vascular Plants

Materials

fossils of extinct lycophytes (*Lepidodendron, Sigillaria*)
fossils of extinct sphenophytes (*Calamites*)
fossils of extinct ferns

Introduction

If we went back in time 300 million years to the Carboniferous period, we would encounter a wide variety of vertebrate amphibians moving about vast swamps dominated by spore-bearing forest trees. Imagine a forest of horsetails and lycophytes the size of trees, amphibians as large as alligators, and enormous dragonflies and roaches! Seedless plants were at their peak during this period and were so prolific that their carbonized remains form the bulk of Earth's coal deposits. Among the most spectacular components of the coal-swamp forest were tree ferns, 100-foot-tall trees belonging to the fossil genera *Lepidodendron* and *Sigillaria,* and 60-foot-tall horsetails assigned to the fossil genus *Calamites* (Figures 3 and 7).

Procedure

Examine flattened fossil stems of *Lepidodendron, Sigillaria, Calamites,* and fossil fern foliage, all of which were recovered from coal mine tailings. Compare these with their living relatives, the lycophytes (club mosses), sphenophytes (horsetails), and ferns, which today are diminutive plants found in restricted habitats.

Results

1. For each division of seedless vascular plants, describe those characteristics that are similar for both living specimens and fossils. For example, do you observe dichotomous branching and similar shape and form of leaves, stems, or sporangia? Refer to the living specimens or your sketches.

   Lycophytes:

   Sphenophytes:

   Ferns:

2. Sketch in the margin of your lab manual the overall structure of the fossils. How would you recognize these fossils at a later date? Label structures where appropriate.

Figure 7.
Seedless vascular plants of the Carboniferous period. Reconstruction of the lycophytes (a) *Lepidodendron* and (b) *Sigillaria*. (c) *Calamites* was a relative of horsetails.

Discussion

The lycophytes, sphenophytes, and ferns were once the giants of the plant kingdom and dominated the landscape. Explain why they are presently restricted to certain habitats and are relatively small in stature.

Questions for Review

1. Complete Table 3, indicating the primitive and advanced features of seedless vascular plants relative to success in land environments. Recall that in this context the term *primitive* means an ancestral trait, while the term *advanced* indicates a derived trait, or adaptation, to land. For example, traits shared with the bryophytes (such as sperm requiring water for fertilization) are primitive, while the presence of vascular tissue is advanced.

Table 3
Primitive and Advanced Features of Seedless Vascular
Plants as They Relate to Adaptation to Land

Primitive Features	Advanced Features

2. For each of the listed features, describe its contribution, if any, to the success of land plants.

   gametangium

   cuticle

   rhizoid

   motile sperm

   vascular tissue

   gemma

3. Complete Table 4. Identify the function of the structures listed. Indicate whether they are part of the gametophyte or sporophyte generation, and provide an example of a plant that has this structure.

Table 4

Structures and Functions of the Bryophytes and Seedless Vascular Plants

Structure	Function	Sporophyte/ Gametophyte	Example
Antheridium			
Archegonium			
Spore			
Gamete			
Rhizome			
Gemma			
Sporangium			
Strobilus			
Sorus			

4. What is the major difference between the alternation of generations in the life cycles of bryophytes and seedless vascular plants?

Applying Your Knowledge

1. The fossil record provides little information about ancient mosses. Do you think that bryophytes could ever have been large tree-sized plants? Provide evidence from your investigations to support your answer.

2. On a walk through a botanical garden, you notice a small leafy plant that is growing along the edge of a small stream in a shady nook. You hypothesize that this plant is a lycophyte. What information can you gather to test your hypothesis?

3. German scientists studied air pollution from heavy metals (cadmium, copper, lead, nickel, and zinc) by analyzing the concentration of these metals in moss samples. They compared mosses collected between 1845 and 1974, which were preserved as herbarium specimens, with mosses collected in 1991. In general, the 1991 mosses had lower heavy metal concentrations. These results were attributed to increased air pollution controls. Based on your knowledge of the structure of the moss gametophyte, can you suggest one or more reasons why mosses are particularly useful indicators of air pollution?

4. Heterospory occasionally occurs in lycophytes and ferns, and in all seed plants. Botanists are convinced that heterospory must have originated more than once in the evolution of plants. Can you suggest one or more advantages that heterospory might provide to plants?

References

Herpin, U., B. Markert, V. Wechert, J. Berklekamp, K. Friese, U. Siewers, and H. Lieth. "Retrospective Analysis of Heavy Metal Concentrations at Selected Locations in the Federal Republic of Germany Using Moss Materials from a Herbarium," *Science of the Total Environment,* 1997, vol. 205, pp. 1–12.

Mauseth, J. D. *Botany: An Introduction to Plant Biology,* 2nd ed. Philadelphia, PA: Saunders College Publishing, 1995.

Moore, R., W. D. Clark, and D. Vodopich. *Botany,* 2nd ed. Dubuque, IA: WCB/McGraw-Hill, 1998.

Raven, P. H., R. F. Evert, and S. E. Eichhorn. *Biology of Plants,* 6th ed. New York: W. H. Freeman Publishers, 1999.

Websites

Links to images of horsetails:

http://www.wisc.edu/botit/systematics/Phyla/Sphenophyta/ Sphenophyta.html

Links to images of whisk ferns:

http://www.wisc.edu/botit/systematics/Phyla/Psilophyta/ Psilophyta.html

Links to images of lycophytes:

http://www.wisc.edu/botit/systematics/Phyla/Lycophyta/ Lycophyta.html

Photo Credits

5b: ©James W. Richardson/Visuals Unlimited.

Art Credits

3, 7: Adapted from James D. Mauseth, *Botany: An Introduction to Plant Biology*, fig. 23.3, p. 667 (Sudbury, MA: Jones and Bartlett Publishers, 1991), www.jbpub.com. Reprinted with permission.

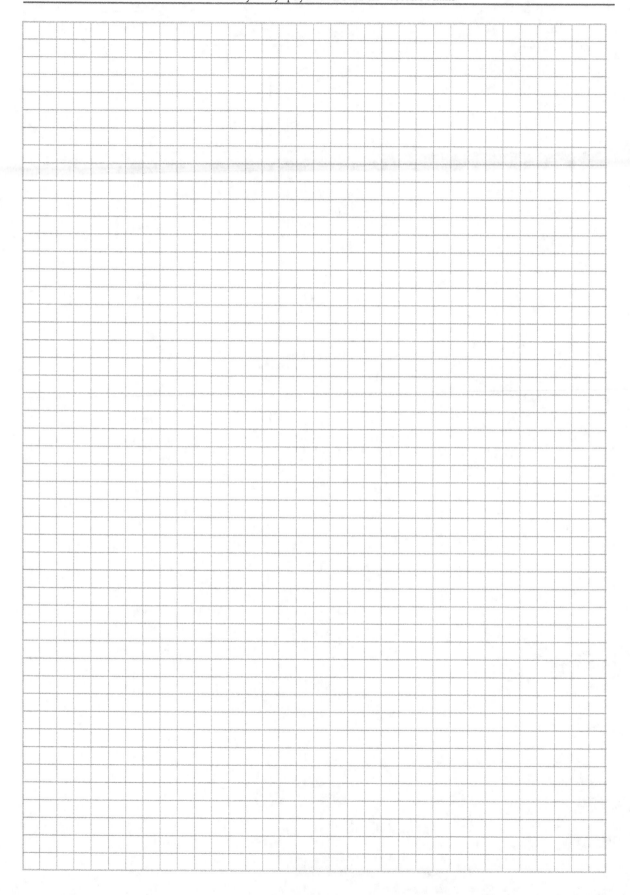

Plant Diversity II: Seed Plants

 Before lab, read the following material on gymnosperms and angiosperms and complete Table 1 by listing (and comparing) the traits of each.

Laboratory Objectives

After completing this lab topic, you should be able to:

1. Identify examples of the divisions of seed plants.
2. Describe the life cycle of a gymnosperm (pine tree) and an angiosperm.
3. Describe features of flowers that ensure pollination by insects, birds, bats, and wind.
4. Describe factors influencing pollen germination.
5. Identify types of fruits, recognize examples, and describe dispersal mechanisms.
6. Relate the structures of seed plants to their functions in the land environment.
7. Compare the significant features of life cycles for various land plants and state their evolutionary importance.
8. Summarize major trends in the evolution of land plants and provide evidence from your laboratory investigations.

Gymnosperms

For over 500 million years, plants have been adapting to the rigors of the land environment. The nonvascular bryophytes with their small and simple bodies survived in moist habitats, habitats moist at least for part of their life cycle. During the cool Carboniferous period, vascular seedless plants dominated the landscape of the swamp forests that covered much of the earth. Although these plants were more complex and better adapted to the challenges of the land environment, they still were dependent on water for sperm to swim to the egg. During the Mesozoic era, 150 million years ago, Earth became warmer and drier and the swamp forests declined, presenting another challenge to terrestrial plants and animals. Earth at that time was a world dominated by reptilian vertebrates, including the flying, running, and climbing dinosaurs. The landscape was dominated by a great

From *Investigating Biology,* Fourth Edition, Judith Giles Morgan and M. Eloise Brown Carter. Copyright © 2002 Pearson Education, Inc., publishing as Benjamin Cummings. All rights reserved.

variety of seed-bearing plants called **gymnosperms** (literally, "naked seeds"), which in the Carboniferous period had been restricted to dry sites. During the Mesozoic, a number of distinct gymnosperm groups diversified, and a few of the spore-bearing plants survived.

Vertebrate animals became fully terrestrial during the Mesozoic with the emergence of reptiles, which were free from a dependence on water for sexual reproduction and development. The development of the amniotic egg along with an internal method of fertilization made this major transition possible. The amniotic egg carries its own water supply and nutrients, permitting early embryonic development to occur on dry land, a great distance from external water. In an analogous manner, the gymnosperms became free from dependence on water through the development of a process of internal fertilization via the pollen grain and development of a seed, which contains a dormant embryo with a protective cover and special nutrient tissue.

Several features of the gymnosperms have been responsible for their success. They have reduced (smaller-sized) gametophytes; the male gametophyte is a multinucleated pollen grain, and the female gametophyte is small and retained within the sporangium in the ovule of the sporophyte generation. The pollen grain is desiccation resistant and adapted for wind pollination, removing the necessity for fertilization in a watery medium. The pollen tube conveys the sperm nucleus to an egg cell, and the embryonic sporophyte develops within the gametophyte tissues, which are protected by the previous sporophyte generation. The resulting seed is not only protected from environmental extremes, but also is packed with nutritive materials and can be dispersed away from the parent plant. In addition, gymnosperms have advanced vascular tissues: xylem for transporting water and nutrients and phloem for transporting photosynthetic products. The xylem cells are called *tracheids* and are more efficient for transport than those of the seedless vascular plants.

Angiosperms

A visit to Earth 60 million years ago, during the late Cretaceous period, would reveal a great diversity of mammals and birds and a landscape dominated by **flowering plants,** or **angiosperms** (division **Anthophyta**). Ultimately, these plants would diversify and become the most numerous, widespread, and important plants on Earth. Angiosperms now occupy well over 90% of the vegetated surface of Earth and contribute virtually 100% of our agricultural food plants.

The evolution of the flower resulted in enormous advances in the efficient transfer and reception of pollen. Whereas gymnosperms are all wind-pollinated, producing enormous amounts of pollen that reach the appropriate species by chance, the process of flower pollination is mediated by specific agents—insects, birds, and bats—in addition to water and wind. Pollination agents such as the insect are attracted to the flower with its rewards of nectar and pollen. Animal movements provide precise placement of pollen on the receptive portion of the female structures, increasing the probability of fertilization. The process also enhances the opportunity for cross-fertilization among distant plants and therefore the possibility of increased genetic variation.

Angiosperm reproduction follows the trend for reduction in the size of the gametophyte. The pollen grain is the male gametophyte, and the eight-nucleated **embryo sac** is all that remains of the female gametophyte. This generation continues to be protected and dependent on the adult sporophyte plant. The female gametophyte provides nutrients for the developing sporophyte embryo through a unique triploid **endosperm** tissue. Another unique feature of angiosperms is the **fruit.** The seeds of the angiosperm develop within the flower ovary, which matures into the fruit. This structure provides protection and enhances dispersal of the young sporophyte into new habitats.

In addition to advances in reproductive biology, the angiosperms evolved other advantageous traits. All gymnosperms are trees or shrubs, with a large investment in woody, persistent tissue; and their life cycles are long (5 or more years before they begin to reproduce and 2 to 3 years to produce a seed). Flowering plants, on the other hand, can be woody, but many are herbaceous, with soft tissues that survive from one to a few years. It is possible for angiosperms to go from seed to seed in less than one year. As you perform the exercises in this lab, think about the significance of this fact in terms of the evolution of this group. How might generation length affect the rate of evolution? Angiosperms also have superior conducting tissues. Xylem tissue is composed of *tracheids* (as in gymnosperms), but also contains large-diameter, open-ended *vessels.* The phloem cells, called *sieve-tube members,* provide more efficient transport of the products of photosynthesis.

Review the characteristics of gymnosperms and angiosperms described in this introduction, and summarize in Table 1 the advantages of these groups relative to their success on land. You should be able to list several characteristics for each. At the end of the lab, you will be asked to modify and complete the table, based on your investigations.

You will want to return to this table after the laboratory to be sure that the table is complete and that you are familiar with all these important features.

EXERCISE 1
Gymnosperms

The term *gymnosperms* refers to a diverse group of seed plants that do not produce flowers. Although they share many characteristics, including the production of pollen, they represent four distinct groups, or divisions. In this exercise, you will observe members of these divisions and investigate the life cycle of a pine, one of the most common gymnosperms.

Table 1
Traits for Gymnosperms and Angiosperms
Relative to Their Success on Land

	Adaptation to the Land Environment
Gymnosperms	
Angiosperms	

Lab Study A. Divisions of Gymnosperms

Materials

living or pressed examples of conifers, ginkgos, cycads, and Mormon tea

Introduction

Gymnosperms are composed of several divisions. The largest and best known is Coniferophyta, which includes pines and other cone-bearing trees and shrubs. Cycads, which have a palmlike appearance, are found primarily in tropical regions scattered around the world. Ginkgos, with their flat fan-shaped leaves, are native to Asia and are prized as urban trees. An extract of *Ginkgo* is used as an herbal medicine purported to improve memory. Gnetophyta is composed of three distinct and unusual groups of plants: gnetums, which are primarily vines of Asia, Africa, and South America; *Welwitschia,* a rare desert plant with two leathery leaves; and Mormon tea (*Ephedra*), desert shrubs of North and Central America. Compounds from *Ephedra*, ephedrines, used in diet aids and decongestants, have raised serious concerns due to side effects including cardiac arrest.

Procedure

1. Observe demonstration examples of all divisions of gymnosperms and be able to recognize their representatives. Note any significant ecological and economic role for these plants.
2. Record your observations in Table 2.

Table 2
Divisions of Gymnosperms

Divisions	Examples	Characteristics/Comments
Coniferophyta		
Ginkgophyta		
Cycadophyta		
Gnetophyta		

Results

1. In the margin of your manual, sketch the overall structure of the plants. Label structures where appropriate.
2. Are there any reproductive structures present for these plants? If so, make notes in the margin of your lab manual.

Discussion

1. What are the key characteristics shared by all gymnosperms?

2. What is the ecological role of conifers in forest systems?

3. What economically important products are provided by conifers?

Lab Study B. Pine Life Cycle

Materials

living or preserved pine branch,
   male and female cones
   (1, 2, and 3 years old)
fresh or dried pine pollen or
   prepared slide of pine pollen

coverslips
prepared slides of male and female
   pine cones
colored pencils
slides

 Review the pine life cycle (Figure 1) before you begin. Follow along as you complete the exercise.

Introduction

All gymnosperms are **wind-pollinated** trees or shrubs, most bearing unisexual, male, and female reproductive structures on different parts of the same plant. Gymnosperms are **heterosporous,** producing two kinds of spores: male **microspores,** which develop into **pollen,** and female **megaspores.** The megaspore develops into the female gametophyte, which is not free-living as with ferns but retained within the **megasporangium** and nourished by the sporophyte parent plant. Numerous pollen grains (the male gametophytes) are produced in each **microsporangium,** and when they are mature they are released into the air and conveyed by wind currents to the female cone. **Pollen tubes** grow through the tissue of the megasporangium, and the **sperm nucleus** is released to fertilize the egg. After fertilization, development results in the formation of an **embryo.** A **seed** is a dormant embryo embedded in nutrient tissue of the female gametophyte and surrounded by the hardened sporangium wall, or **seed coat.**

 Having trouble with life cycles? The key to success is to determine where meiosis occurs and to remember the ploidal level for the gametophyte and sporophyte.

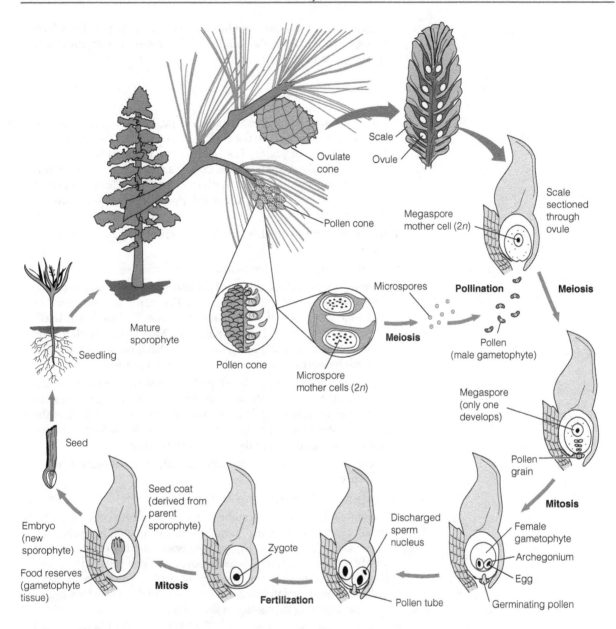

Figure 1.
Pine life cycle. Observe the structures and processes as described in Exercise 1.
Using colored pencils, indicate the structures that are haploid or diploid. Circle the terms
mitosis, meiosis, *and* fertilization.

Procedure

1. Pine sporophyte.
    a. Examine the pine branch and notice the arrangement of leaves in a
       bundle. A new twig at the end of the branch is in the process of pro-
       ducing new clusters of leaves. Is this plant haploid or diploid?

    b. Examine the small **cones** produced at the end of the pine branch on this specimen or others in lab. Recall that cones contain clusters of sporangia. What important process occurs in the sporangia?

    c. Locate an ovulate cone and a pollen cone. Elongated male **pollen cones** are present only in the spring, producing pollen within overlapping bracts, or scales. The small, more rounded female cones (which look like miniature pine cones) are produced on stem tips in the spring and are called **ovulate cones.** Female cones persist for several years. Observe the overlapping scales, which contain the sporangia.

    d. In the margin of your lab manual, sketch observations for future reference.

2.   Male gametophyte—development in pollen cones.

    a. Examine a longitudinal section of the pollen cone on a prepared slide and identify its parts. Observe that pollen cones are composed of radiating scales, each of which carries two elongated sacs on its lower surface. The sacs are the **microsporangia. Microspore mother cells** within microsporangia divide by meiosis. Each produces four haploid **microspores,** which develop into **pollen grains.**

    b. Observe a slide of pine pollen. If pollen is available, you can make a wet mount. Note the wings on either side of the grain. The pollen grain is the greatly reduced male gametophyte. The outer covering of the pollen is desiccation resistant. Once mature, pollen will be wind dispersed, sifting down into the scales of the female cones.

    c. Sketch, in the margin of your lab manual, observations for future reference.

3.   Female gametophyte—development in ovulate cones.

    a. Examine a longitudinal section of a young ovulate cone on a prepared slide. Note the **ovule** (containing the megasporangium) on the upper surface of the scales. Diploid **megaspore mother cells** contained inside will produce haploid **megaspores,** the first cells of the gametophyte generation. In the first year of ovulate cone development, pollen sifts into the soft bracts (pollination) and the pollen tube begins to grow, digesting the tissues of the ovule.

    b. Observe a second-year cone at your lab bench. During the second year, the ovule develops a multicellular female gametophyte with two archegonia in which an egg will form. Fertilization will not occur until the second year, when the pollen tube releases a sperm nucleus into the archegonium, where it unites with the egg to form the **zygote.** In each ovule only one of the archegonia and its zygote develops into a seed.

    c. Observe a mature cone at your lab bench. The development of the embryo sporophyte usually takes another year. The female gametophyte will provide nutritive materials stored in the seed for the early stages of growth. The outer tissues of the ovule will harden to form the **seed coat.**

    d. In the margin of your lab manual, sketch observations for future reference.

Results

1. Review the structures and processes observed.
2. Using colored pencils, indicate the structures of the pine life cycle in Figure 1 that are haploid or diploid, and circle the processes of mitosis, meiosis, and fertilization.

Discussion

1. What is the function of the wings on the pollen grain?

2. Why is wind-dispersed pollen an important phenomenon in the evolution of plants?

3. Are microspores and megaspores produced by mitosis or meiosis?

4. Can you think of at least two ways in which pine seeds are dispersed?

5. One of the major trends in plant evolution is the reduction in size of the gametophytes. Describe the male and female gametophyte in terms of size and location.

EXERCISE 2
Angiosperms

A unique characteristic of angiosperms (division Anthophyta) is the **carpel**, a vessel in which ovules are enclosed. After fertilization, the ovule develops into a seed (as in the gymnosperms), while the carpel matures into a fruit (unique to angiosperms). Other important aspects of angiosperm reproduction include additional reduction of the gametophyte, double fertilization, and an increase in the rapidity of the reproduction process.

The **flowers** of angiosperms are composed of male and female reproductive structures, which are frequently surrounded by attractive or protective leaflike structures collectively known as the **perianth**. The flower functions both to protect the developing gametes and to ensure pollination and fertilization. Although many angiosperm plants are self-fertile, cross-fertilization is important in maintaining genetic diversity. Plants, rooted and stationary, often require transfer agents to complete fertilization. A variety of insects, birds, and mammals transfer pollen from flower to flower. The pollen then germinates into a pollen tube and grows through the female carpel to deliver the sperm to the egg.

Plants must attract pollinators to the flower. What are some features of flowers that attract pollinators? Color and scent are important, as is the shape of the flower. Nectar and pollen provide nutritive rewards for the pollinators as well. The shape and form of some of the flowers are structured to accommodate pollinators of specific size and structure, providing landing platforms, guidelines, and even special mechanisms for the placement of pollen on body parts. While the flower is encouraging the visitation by one type of pollinator, it also may be excluding visitation by others. The more specific the relationship between flower and pollinator, the more probable that the pollen of that species will be successfully transferred. But many successful flowers have no specific adaptations for particular pollinators and are visited by a wide variety of pollinators.

Some plants do not have colorful, showy flowers and are rather inconspicuous, often dull in color, and lacking a perianth. These plants are usually wind-pollinated, producing enormous quantities of pollen and adapted to catch pollen in the wind.

The origin and diversification of angiosperms cannot be understood apart from the coevolutionary role of animals in the reproductive process. Colorful petals, strong scents, nectars, food bodies, and unusual perianth shapes all relate to pollinator visitation. Major trends in the evolution of angiosperms involve the development of mechanisms to exploit a wide variety of pollinators.

In Lab Study A, you will investigate a variety of flowers, observing their shape, structure, and traits that might attract pollinators of various kinds. Following this, in Lab Study B, you will use a key to identify the probable pollinators for some of these flowers. You will follow the life cycle of the lily in Lab Study C and complete the lab by using another key to identify types of fruits and their dispersal mechanisms.

Lab Study A. Flower Morphology

Materials

living flowers provided by the instructor and/or students
stereoscopic microscope

Introduction

Working in teams of two students, you will investigate the structure of the flower (Figure 2). The instructor will provide a variety of flowers, and you may have brought some with you to lab. You will need to take apart each flower carefully to determine its structure, since it is unlikely that all your flowers will follow the simple diagram used to illustrate the structures. Your observations will be the basis for predicting probable pollinators in Lab Study B.

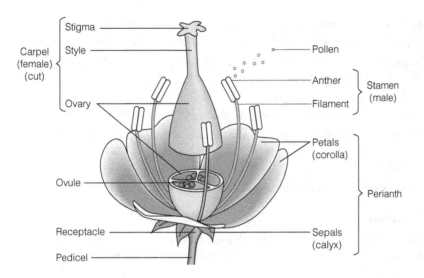

Figure 2.
Flower structures. Determine the structures of flowers in the laboratory by reviewing this general diagram.

Procedure

1. Examine fresh flowers of four different species, preferably with different floral characteristics.

2. Identify the parts of each flower using Figure 2 and the list provided following the heading Floral Parts. You may be able to determine the floral traits for large, open flowers by simply observing. However, most flowers will require that you remove the floral structures from the outside toward the center of the flower. Some flowers or structures may require the use of the stereoscopic microscope. For example, the ovary is positively identified by the presence of tiny crystal-like ovules, and these are best seen with the stereoscopic scope.

3. In the margin of your lab manual, sketch any flower shapes or structures that you might need to refer to in the future.

4. Record the results of your observations in Table 3. You will determine pollinators in Lab Study B.

Floral Parts

Pedicel: stalk that supports the flower.

Receptacle: tip of the pedicel where the flower parts attach.

Sepal: outer whorl of bracts, which may be green, brown, or colored like the petals; may appear as small scales or be petal-like.

Calyx: all the sepals, collectively.

Petal: colored, white, or even greenish whorl of bracts located just inside the sepals.

Corolla: all the petals, collectively.

Stamen: pollen-bearing structure, composed of filament and anther.

Filament: thin stalk that supports the anther.

Anther: pollen-producing structure.

Carpel: female reproductive structure, composed of the stigma, style, and ovary, often pear-shaped and located in the center of the flower.

Stigma: receptive tip of the carpel, often sticky or hairy, where pollen is placed; important to pollen germination.

Style: tissue connecting stigma to ovary, often long and narrow, but may be short or absent; pollen must grow through this tissue to fertilize the egg.

Ovary: base of carpel; protects ovules inside, matures to form the fruit.

Results

Summarize your observations of flower structure in Table 3.

Discussion

What structures or characteristics did you observe in your (or other teams') investigations that you predict are important to pollination?

Lab Study B. Pollinators

Materials

living flowers provided by the instructor and/or students
stereoscopic microscope

Introduction

Flowers with inconspicuous sepals and petals are usually pollinated by wind. Most showy flowers are pollinated by animals. Some pollinators tend to be attracted to particular floral traits, and, in turn, some groups of plants have coevolved with a particular pollination agent that ensures successful reproduction. Other flowers are generalists, pollinated by a variety of organisms, and still others may be visited by only one specific pollinator. Based on the floral traits that attract common pollinators (bees, flies, butterflies, and hummingbirds), you will predict the probable pollinator for some of your flowers using a dichotomous key. (Remember, *dichotomous* refers to the branching pattern and means "divided into two parts.")

In biology, we use a key to systematically separate groups of organisms based on sets of characteristics. Most keys are based on couplets, or pairs of characteristics, from which you must choose one or the other, thus, the term *dichotomous*. For example, the first choice of characteristics in a couplet might be *plants with showy flowers and a scent,* and the other choice in the pair might be *plants with tiny, inconspicuous flowers with no scent.* You must choose one or the other statement. In the next step, you would choose from a second pair of statements listed directly below your first choice. With each choice, you would narrow the group more and more until, as in this case, the pollinator is identified. *Each couplet or pair of statements from which you must choose will be identified by the same letter or number.*

Table 3
Flower Morphology and Pollinators

Features	Plant Names			
	1	2	3	4
Number of petals				
Number of sepals				
Parts absent (petals, stamens, etc.)				
Color				
Scent (+/–)				
Nectar (+/–)				
Shape (including corolla shape: tubular, star, etc.)				
Special features (landing platform, guidelines, nectar spur, etc.)				
Predicted pollinator (see Lab Study B)				

Key to Pollination

I. Sepals and petals reduced or inconspicuous; feathery or relatively large stigma; flower with no odor **wind**

I. Sepals and/or petals large, easily identified; stigma not feathery; flower with or without odor

   A. Sepals and petals white or subdued (greenish or burgundy); distinct odor

      1. Odor strong, heavy, sweet **moth**

      1. Odor strong, fermenting or fruitlike; flower parts and pedicel strong **bat**

      1. Odor of sweat, feces, or decaying meat **fly**

   A. Sepals and/or petals colored; odor may or may not be present

      1. Flower shape regular or irregular,* but not tubular

         a. Flower shape irregular; sepals or petals blue, yellow, or orange; petal adapted to serve as a "landing platform"; may have dark lines on petals; sweet, fragrant odor **bee**

         a. Flower shape regular; odor often fruity, spicy, sweet, or carrionlike **beetle**

      1. Flower shape tubular

         a. Strong, sweet odor **butterfly**

         a. Little or no odor; flower usually red **hummingbird**

*A regular flower shape is one that has radial symmetry (like a daisy or carnation), with similar parts (such as petals) having similar size and shape. Irregular flowers have bilateral symmetry.

Procedure

Using the key above, classify the flowers used in Lab Study A based on their floral traits and method of pollination.

Results

1. Record your results in Table 3.
2. If you made sketches of any of your flowers, you may want to indicate the pollinator associated with that flower.

Discussion

1. Review the Key to Pollination and describe the characteristics of flowers that are adapted for pollination by each of the following agents:

   a. wind

   b. hummingbird

   c. bat

2. Discuss with your lab partner other ways in which keys are used in biology. Record your answers in the space provided.

Lab Study C. Angiosperm Life Cycle

Materials

pollen tube growth medium in
   dropper bottles
dropper bottle of water
petri dish with filter paper to
   fit inside
prepared slides of lily anthers
   and ovary

dissecting probe
brush bristles
compound microscope
flowers for pollen

Introduction

In this lab study, you will study the life cycle of flowering plants, including the formation of pollen, pollination, fertilization of the egg, and formation of the seed and fruit. You will also investigate the germination of the pollen grain as it grows toward the egg cell.

 Refer to Figures 2 (flower structures) and 3 (angiosperm life cycle) as you complete the exercise.

Procedure

1. Pollen grain—the male gametophyte.
    a. Examine a prepared slide of a cross section through the **stamens** of *Lilium.* The slide shows six anthers and may include a centrally located ovary that contains ovules.
    b. Observe a single **anther,** which is composed of four **anther sacs** (microsporangia). Note the formation of **microspores** (with a single nucleus) from diploid **microspore mother cells.** You may also see mature **pollen grains** with two nuclei.
2. Development of the female gametophyte.
    a. Examine a prepared slide of the *Lilium* ovary and locate the developing ovules. Each **ovule,** composed of the megasporangium and other tissues, contains a **megaspore mother cell** (diploid), which produces **megaspores** (haploid), only one of which survives. The megaspore will divide three times by mitosis to produce the eight nuclei in the **embryo sac,** which is the greatly reduced female gametophyte. Note that angiosperms do not even produce an archegonium.

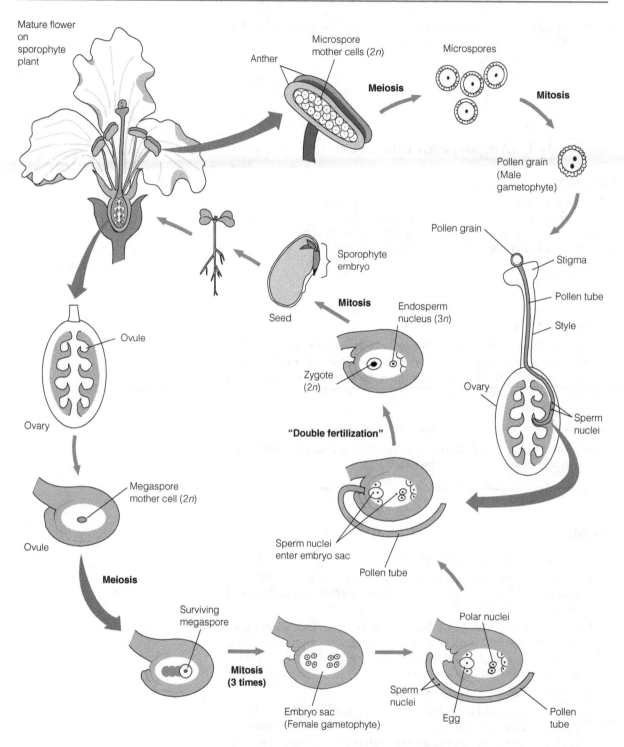

Mature flower on sporophyte plant

Anther

Microspore mother cells (2*n*)

Meiosis

Microspores

Mitosis

Pollen grain (Male gametophyte)

Pollen grain

Stigma

Pollen tube

Style

Sporophyte embryo

Seed

Mitosis

Endosperm nucleus (3*n*)

Zygote (2*n*)

Ovary

Sperm nuclei

Ovule

Ovary

"Double fertilization"

Sperm nuclei enter embryo sac

Pollen tube

Megaspore mother cell (2*n*)

Ovule

Meiosis

Surviving megaspore

Mitosis (3 times)

Embryo sac (Female gametophyte)

Polar nuclei

Sperm nuclei

Egg

Pollen tube

Figure 3.
Angiosperm life cycle. Observe the structures and processes as described in Exercise 2. *Using colored pencils, indicate the structures that are haploid or diploid. Circle the terms* mitosis, meiosis, *and* double fertilization.

b. Your slide will not contain all stages of development, and it is almost impossible to find a section that includes all eight nuclei. Locate the three nuclei near the opening to the ovule. One of these is called the **egg cell.** The two nuclei in the center are the **polar nuclei.**

3. Pollination and fertilization.

When pollen grains are mature, the anthers split and the pollen is released. When pollen reaches the stigma, it germinates to produce a **pollen tube,** which grows down the style and eventually comes into contact with the opening to the ovule. During this growth, one pollen nucleus divides into two **sperm nuclei.** One sperm nucleus fuses with the egg to form the **zygote,** and the second fuses with the two polar nuclei to form the triploid **endosperm,** which will develop into a rich nutritive material for the support and development of the embryo. The fusion of the two sperm nuclei with nuclei of the embryo sac is referred to as **double fertilization.** Formation of triploid endosperm and double fertilization are unique to angiosperms.

Once the pollen grain is deposited on the stigma of the flower, it must grow through the stylar tissue to reach the ovule. You will examine pollen tube growth by placing pollen in pollen growth medium to stimulate germination. Pollen from some plants germinates easily; for others a very specific chemical environment is required. Work with a partner, following the next steps.

a. Using a dissecting probe, transfer some pollen from the anthers of one of the plants available in the lab to a slide on which there are 2 to 3 drops of pollen tube growth medium and a few brush bristles or grains of sand (to avoid crushing the pollen).

b. Examine the pollen under the compound microscope. Observe the shape and surface features of the pollen.

c. Prepare a humidity chamber by placing moistened filter paper in a petri dish. Place the slide in the petri dish, and place it in a warm environment.

d. Examine the pollen after 30 minutes and again after 60 minutes to observe pollen tube growth. The pollen tubes should appear as long, thin tubes extending from the surface or pores in the pollen grain.

e. Record your results in Table 4 in the Results section. Indicate the plant name and the times when pollen tube germination was observed.

4. Seed and fruit development.

The zygote formed at fertilization undergoes rapid mitotic divisions, forming the embryo. The endosperm also divides; the mature ovule forms a seed. At the same time, the surrounding ovary and other floral tissues are forming the fruit. In Lab Study D, you will investigate the types of fruits and their function in dispersal.

Results

1. Review the structures and processes observed in the angiosperm life cycle, Figure 3. Indicate the haploid and diploid structures in the life cycle, using two different colored pencils.

Having trouble with life cycles? The key to success is to determine where meiosis occurs and to remember the ploidal level for the gametophyte and sporophyte.

2. Sketch observations of slides in the margin of your lab manual for later reference.
3. Record the results of pollen germination studies in Table 4. Compare your results with those of other teams who used different plants. This is particularly important if your pollen did not germinate.

Table 4
Results of Pollen Germination Studies

Plant Name	30 min (+/−)	60 min (+/−)

Discussion

1. What part of the life cycle is represented by the mature pollen grain?

2. How does the female gametophyte in angiosperms differ from the female gametophyte in gymnosperms?

3. Do you think that all pollen germinates indiscriminately on all stigmas? How might pollen germination and growth be controlled?

Lab Study D. Fruits and Dispersal

Materials

variety of fruits provided by the instructor and/or students

Introduction

The seed develops from the ovule, and inside is the embryo and its nutritive tissues. The fruit develops from the ovary or from other tissues in the flower. It provides protection for the seeds, and both the seed and the fruit may be involved in dispersal of the sporophyte embryo.

Procedure

1. Examine the fruits and seeds on demonstration.
2. Use the Key to Fruits on the next page to help you complete Table 5. Remember to include the dispersal mechanisms for fruits and their seeds in the table.

Results

1. Record in Table 5 the fruit type for each of the fruits keyed. Share results with other teams so that you have information for all fruits in the lab.

Table 5
Fruit Types and Dispersal Mechanisms

Plant Name	Fruit Type	Dispersal Method

2. For each fruit, indicate the probable method of dispersal—for example, wind, water, gravity, ingestion by birds, mammals, or insects, or adhesion to fur and socks.
3. For some fruits, the seeds rather than the fruit are adapted for dispersal. In the milkweed, for example, the winged seeds are contained in a dry ovary. Indicate in Table 5 if the seeds have structures to enhance dispersal. Recall that seeds are inside fruits. The dandelion "seed" is really a fruit with a fused ovary and seed coat.

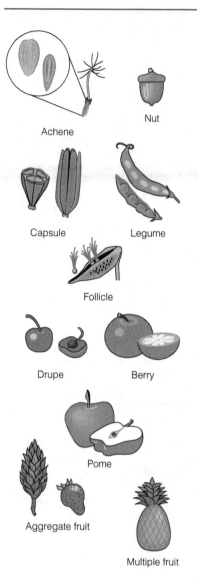

Achene

Nut

Capsule

Legume

Follicle

Drupe

Berry

Pome

Aggregate fruit

Multiple fruit

Key to Fruits

I. Simple fruits (one ovary)
  A. Dry fruits (at maturity)
    1. Fruits with one seed
      a. Ovary wall and seed coat are fused   **achene***
      a. Ovary wall hard or woody but can be separated from the seed   **nut**
    1. Fruits with two to many seeds
      a. Ovary with several cavities (seen when cut in cross section) and several to many seeds   **capsule**
      a. Ovary with one cavity
        b. Mature ovary opens along both sides   **legume**
        b. Mature ovary opens along one side   **follicle**
  A. Fleshy fruits
    1. Ovary with one seed, which is surrounded by a very hard stone (outer covering of the seed is formed from the inner ovary wall)   **drupe**
    1. Ovary with many seeds; does not have a "stone"
      a. All of mature ovary tissue is soft and fleshy; surrounding flower tissue does not develop into fruit   **berry†**
      a. Fleshy fruit develops in part from surrounding tissue of the flower (base of sepals and petals); therefore, ovary wall seen as "core" around seeds   **pome**
I. Compound fruits (more than one ovary)
  A. Fruit formed from ovaries of many flowers   **multiple fruit**
  A. Fruit formed from several ovaries in one flower   **aggregate fruit**

*In the grass family, an achene is called a **grain.**
†Berries of some families have special names: citrus family = **hesperidium**; squash family = **pepo.**

Discussion

1. How might dry fruits be dispersed? Fleshy fruits?

2. Describe the characteristics of an achene, drupe, and berry.

Questions for Review

1. Return to Table 1 and modify your entries and complete your comparison of gymnosperms and angiosperms.

2. Identify the function of each of the following structures found in seed plants. Consider their function in the land environment.

   pollen grain:

   microsporangium:

   flower:

   carpel:

   seed:

   fruit:

   endosperm:

3. Plants have evolved a number of characteristics that attract animals and ensure pollination, but what are the benefits to animals in this relationship?

4. Why is internal fertilization essential for true terrestrial living?

Applying Your Knowledge

1. Explain how the rise in prominence of one major group (angiosperms, for example) does not necessarily result in the total replacement of a previously dominant group (gymnosperms, for example).

2. Complete Table 6. Compare mosses, ferns, conifers, and flowering plants relative to sexual life cycles and adaptations to the land environment.

3. How have gymnosperm ovules evolved to withstand desiccation and herbivorous animals?

Table 6
Comparison of Important Characteristics of Land Plants

Features	Moss	Fern	Conifer	Flowering Plant
Gametophyte or sporophyte dominant				
Vascular tissue (+/–)				
Seed (+/–)				
Fruit (+/–)				
Water required for fertilization				
Pollen grain (+/–)				
Homosporous or heterosporous				
Examples				

4. Your neighbor's vegetable garden is being attacked by Japanese beetles, so she dusts her garden with an insecticide. Now, to her dismay, she realizes that the beans and squash are no longer producing. Explain to your neighbor the relationship among flowers, fruits (vegetables, in the gardening language), and insects.

5. In angiosperms, an abundance of pollen is transferred by insects to the stigma. Later, pollen grains germinate to produce pollen tubes that race through the style in their bid to fertilize a limited number of egg cells within the ovules. Explain how this process of gamete competition could be of selective advantage.

6. Describe the major trends in the evolution of land plants.

Investigative Extensions

Pollen germinates easily in the lab for some species and not at all for others. In some species, a biochemical signal is required from the stigma to initiate germination. If the pollen has not germinated after 30 minutes, you can design an experiment to test the hypothesis that a substance in the stigma is necessary for pollen germination. Mince a small part of the stigma in sucrose and then add it to the slide preparation. The percent sucrose in the growth medium can also be varied. Try 10%, then doubling and halving the sucrose concentration in the growth medium. Some cultivated plants are simply sterile, so do not expect positive results for all species.

References

Mauseth, J. D. *Botany: An Introduction to Plant Biology,* 2nd ed. Philadelphia, PA: Saunders College Publishing, 1995.

Moore, R., W. D. Clark, and D. Vodopich. *Botany,* 2nd ed. Dubuque, IA: WCB/McGraw-Hill, 1998.

Raven, P. H., R. F. Evert, and S. E. Eichhorn. *Biology of Plants,* 6th ed. New York: W. H. Freeman Publishers, 1999.

Art Credits

3: Adapted from Neil Campbell, Jane Reece, and Larry Mitchell, *Biology,* 5th ed. (Menlo Park, CA: Benjamin/ Cummings, 1999), ©1999 The Benjamin/Cummings Publishing Company.

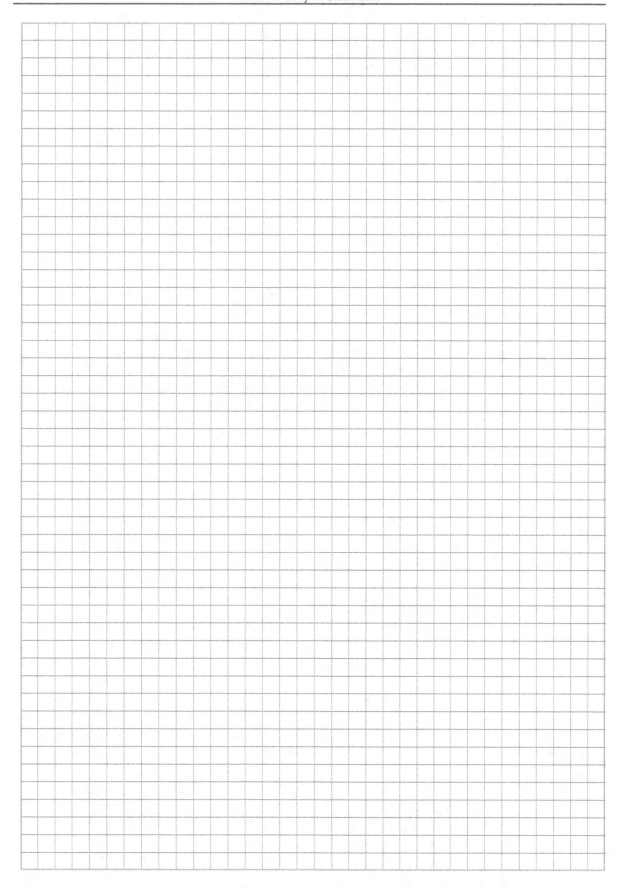

Animal Diversity I

Laboratory Objectives

After completing this lab topic, you should be able to:

1. Compare the anatomy of the representative animals, describing similarities and differences in organs and body form that allow the animal to carry out body functions.
2. Discuss how these similarities and differences may indicate phylogenetic relationships.
3. Discuss the relationship between body form and the lifestyle or niche of the organism.
4. List five characteristics that are criteria for major branching points among less complex animal groups in the phylogenetic tree.

Introduction

Animals are classified in the domain **Eukarya,** kingdom **Animalia.** They are multicellular organisms and are **heterotrophic,** meaning that they obtain food by ingesting other organisms or their by-products. Careful study of comparative anatomy and embryology reveals many similarities in structure and development, implying an ancestral evolutionary relationship among all animals. Animals are thought to have arisen about 565 million years ago, with most body forms appearing by the end of the Cambrian period. Scientists recognize over 35 major groups of present-day animals based on differences in body architecture. In this and the following lab topic, you will investigate body form and function in examples of eight major groups of animals. You will use these investigations to ask and answer questions about the lifestyle of each animal and the **phylogenetic,** or evolutionary, relationships among the animals.

Since the beginning of the scientific study of animals, scientists have attempted to sort and group closely related organisms. Taxonomists have divided the animal kingdom into two **subkingdoms: Parazoa,** which includes the sponges, and **Eumetazoa,** which includes all other animals. This division is made because the body form of sponges is so different from that of other animals that most biologists think that sponges are not closely related to any other animal groups.

Eumetazoa is further divided on the basis of physical characteristics, such as symmetry and the type of body cavity (coelom), and such basic embryological differences as the number of germ layers present in the embryo and the embryonic development of the digestive tract. Some animals have a

From *Investigating Biology,* Fourth Edition, Judith Giles Morgan and M. Eloise Brown Carter. Copyright © 2002 Pearson Education, Inc., publishing as Benjamin Cummings. All rights reserved.

saclike body form with only one opening into a digestive cavity. Others have two outer openings, a mouth and an anus, and the digestive tract forms essentially a "tube within a tube." Animals with a mouth and an anus are divided into two major groups, depending on the origin of the mouth and the anus. An embryonic structure, the blastopore, develops into a mouth in the **protostomes** and into an anus in the **deuterostomes.**

Zoologists have, somewhat artificially, divided animals into **invertebrates** and **vertebrates,** based on the absence or presence of a backbone. Vertebrates, those animals with a backbone, include only about 5% of total animal species, the remaining 95% being invertebrates. Invertebrates are a heterogeneous group with a diversity of phylogenetic origins. In addition to phylogenetic relationships, many structural and functional adaptive themes related to the size, lifestyle, or environment of the animal appear repeatedly in animal design. Thus, the study of the anatomy of animals can lead both to predictions about their phylogenetic relationships and to conclusions about their lifestyles and environment.

In the next two laboratory periods, you will examine and dissect several invertebrates and observe one vertebrate, relating the morphology of these organisms to their body functions, lifestyles, and phylogenetic relationships.

The animals you will study are the sponge, hydra, planarian, roundworm, clamworm, earthworm, clam (mussel), crayfish, grasshopper, amphioxus (lancelet), and pig. As you study each animal, relate your observations to the unifying themes of this lab: *phylogenetic relationships* and criteria that are the basis for animal classification, the *relationship between form and function,* and the *relationship of the environment and lifestyle to form and function.* The questions at the end of the lab topics will help you do this.

In your comparative study of these organisms, you will investigate 13 characteristics. Before you begin the dissections, become familiar with the following characteristics and their descriptions:

1. *Symmetry.* Is the animal (a) radially symmetrical (parts arranged around a central axis), (b) bilaterally symmetrical (right and left halves are mirror images), or (c) asymmetrical (no apparent symmetry)?

2. *Tissue organization.* Are cells organized into well-defined tissue layers (structural and functional units)? How many distinctive layers are present?

3. *Body cavity.* Is a body cavity present? A body cavity—the space between the gut and body wall—is present only in three-layered organisms, that is, in organisms with the embryonic germ layers ectoderm, mesoderm, and endoderm. There are three types of body forms related to the presence of a body cavity and its type (Figure 1).

    a. Acoelomate, three-layered bodies without a body cavity. Tissue from the mesoderm fills the space where a cavity might be; therefore, the tissue layers closely pack on one another.

    b. Pseudocoelomate, three-layered bodies with a cavity between the endoderm (gut) and mesoderm (muscle).

    c. Eucoelomate (coelomate), three-layered bodies with the coelom, or cavity, *within* the mesoderm (completely surrounded by mesoderm). In coelomate organisms, mesodermal membranes suspend the gut within the body cavity.

a. Acoelomate

b. Pseudocoelomate

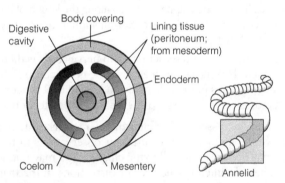

c. Eucoelomate (coelomate)

Figure 1.
Three types of body cavities.
(a) In acoelomate animals, the mesoderm fills the space where a cavity might be. (b) In pseudocoelomate animals, the body cavity lies between tissues derived from endoderm and mesoderm. (c) In eucoelomate (coelomate) animals, the body cavity is lined with mesoderm.

4. *Openings into the digestive tract.* Can you detect where food enters the body and digestive waste exits the body? Some animals have only one opening, which serves as both a mouth and an anus. Others have a body called a "tube within a tube," with an anterior mouth and a posterior anus.

5. *Circulatory system.* Does this animal have open circulation (the blood flows through coelomic spaces in the tissue as well as in blood vessels), or does it have closed circulation (the blood flows entirely through vessels)?

6. *Habitat.* Is the animal terrestrial (lives on land) or aquatic (lives in water)? Aquatic animals may live in marine (sea) or fresh water.

7. *Organs for respiration (gas exchange).* Can you detect the surface where oxygen enters the body and carbon dioxide leaves the body? Many animals use their skin for respiration. Others have special organs, including gills in aquatic organisms and lungs in terrestrial organisms. Insects have a unique system for respiration, using structures called *spiracles* and *tracheae.*

8. *Organs for excretion.* How does the animal rid its body of nitrogenous waste? In many animals, these wastes pass out of the body through the skin by diffusion. In others, there are specialized structures, such as Malpighian tubules, lateral excretory canals, lateral canals with flame cells, structures called *nephridia,* and kidneys.

9. *Type of locomotion.* Does the organism swim, crawl on its belly, walk on legs, burrow in the substrate, or fly? Does it use cellular structures, such as cilia, to glide its body over the substrate?

10. *Support systems.* Is there a skeleton present? Is it an endoskeleton (inside the epidermis or skin of the animal), or is it an exoskeleton (outside the body wall)? Animals with no true skeleton can be supported by water: Fluid within and between cells and in body chambers such as a gastrovascular cavity or coelom provides a "hydrostatic skeleton."

11. *Segmentation.* Can you observe linear repetition of similar body parts? The repetition of similar units, or segments, is called *segmentation.* Segments can be more similar (as in the earthworm) or less similar (as in a lobster). Can you observe any degree of segmentation? Have various segments become modified for different functions?

12. *Appendages.* Are there appendages (organs or parts attached to a trunk or outer body wall)? Are these appendages all along the length of the body, or are they restricted to one area? Are they all similar, or are they modified for different functions?

13. *Type of nervous system.* Do you see a brain and nerve cord? Is there more than one nerve cord? What is the location of the nerve cord(s)? Are sensory organs or structures present? Where and how many? What purpose do such structures serve (for example, eyes for light detection)?

As you carefully study or dissect each organism, refer to these thirteen characteristics, observe the animal, and record your observations in the summary table, that may appear in the following chapter. You may find it helpful to make sketches of difficult structures or dissections in the margin of your lab manual for future reference.

Before you begin this study, become thoroughly familiar with dissection techniques, orientation terms, and planes and sections of the body.

 Wear gloves while dissecting preserved animals.

EXERCISE 1
Phylum Porifera—Sponges (*Scypha*)

Materials

dissecting needle
compound microscope
stereoscopic microscope
preserved and dry bath sponges

prepared slide of *Scypha* in
longitudinal section
preserved *Scypha* in watch glass

Introduction

Sponges are classified in a separate subkingdom, Parazoa, because of their unique body form. You will observe the unique sponge structure by observing first a preserved specimen and then a prepared slide of a section taken through the longitudinal axis of the marine sponge *Scypha*. You will observe other more complex and diverse sponges on demonstration.

Procedure

1. Obtain the preserved sponge *Scypha* and observe its external characteristics using the stereoscopic microscope, comparing your observations with Figure 2a.

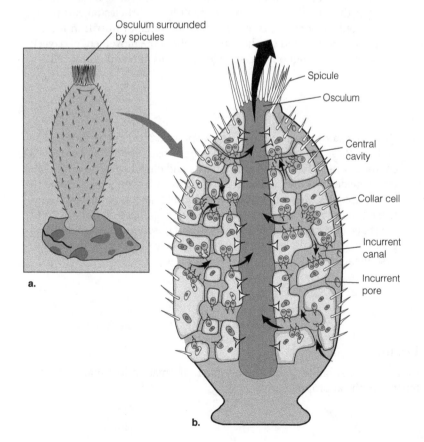

a.

b.

Figure 2.
The sponge *Scypha*. (a) The entire sponge; (b) a longitudinal section through the sponge.

Osculum surrounded by spicules

Spicule

Osculum

Central cavity

Collar cell

Incurrent canal

Incurrent pore

a. Note the vaselike shape of the sponge and the **osculum,** a large opening to the body at one end. The end opposite the osculum attaches the animal to the substrate.

b. Note the invaginations in the body wall, which form numerous folds and channels. You may be able to observe needlelike **spicules** around the osculum and protruding from the surface of the body. These spicules are made of calcium carbonate: They give support and protection to the sponge body and prevent small animals from entering the sponge's internal cavity.

2. Using the compound microscope, examine a prepared slide of a sponge body in longitudinal section and compare it with Figure 2b.

a. Again, locate the osculum. This structure is not a mouth, as its name implies, but an opening used as an outlet for the current of water passing through the body wall and the **central cavity,** or **spongocoel.** The water enters the central cavity from channels and pores in the body. The central cavity is not a digestive tube or body cavity, but is only a channel for water.

b. Note the structure of the body wall. Are cells organized into definite tissue layers, or are they best described as a loose organization of various cell types? Various cells in the body wall carry out the functions of digestion, contractility, secretion of the spicules, and reproduction (some cells develop into sperm and eggs). One cell type unique to sponges is the **choanocyte,** or **collar cell.** These cells line the central cavity and the channels leading into it. Each collar cell has a flagellum extending from its surface. The collective beating of all flagella moves water through the sponge body. Small food particles taken up and digested by collar cells are one major source of nutrition for the sponge. How would you hypothesize about the movement of oxygen and waste throughout the sponge body and into and out of cells?

3. Observe examples of more complex sponges on demonstration. The body of these sponges, sometimes called "bath sponges," contains a complex series of large and small canals and chambers. The same cells that were described in *Scypha* are present in bath sponges, but, in addition to spicules, there is supportive material that consists of a soft proteinaceous substance called **spongin.** These sponges often grow to fit the shape of the space where they live, and observing them gives you a good clue about the symmetry of the sponge body. How would you describe it?

Results

Complete the summary table, filling in all information for sponge characteristics in the appropriate row.

EXERCISE 2
Phylum Cnidaria—Hydras (*Hydra*)

Materials

stereoscopic microscope
compound microscope
living *Hydra* culture
water flea culture
dropper bottles of water, 1% acetic
    acid, and methylene blue

prepared slide of *Hydra* sections
watch glass
depression slide
pipettes and bulbs
microscope slide and coverslip

Introduction

Cnidarians are a diverse group of organisms, all of which have a **tissue grade** of organization, meaning that tissues, but no complex organs, are present. Included in this group are corals, jellies, sea anemones, and Portuguese men-of-war. Most species are marine; however, there are a few freshwater species. Two body forms are present in the life cycle of many of these

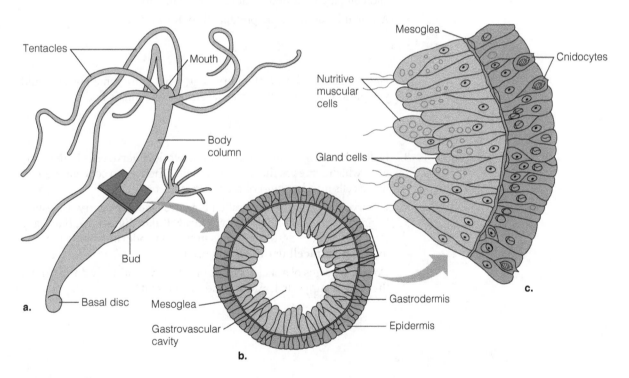

Figure 3.
Hydra. (a) A whole mount of *Hydra*; (b) enlargement showing a cross section through the body wall, revealing two tissue layers; and (c) further enlargement showing details of specialized cells in the body wall, including cnidocytes.

animals—an umbrella-like, free-swimming stage, and a cylindrical, attached or stationary form. The stationary forms often grow into colonies of individuals. In this exercise you will observe some of the unique features of this group by observing the solitary, freshwater organism *Hydra*.

Procedure

1. Place several drops of freshwater pond or culture water in a watch glass or depression slide. Use a dropper to obtain a living hydra from the class culture, and place the hydra in the drop of water. Using a stereoscopic microscope, observe the hydra structure and compare it with Figure 3a. Note any movement, the symmetry, and any body structures present. Note the **tentacles** that surround the "mouth," the only opening into the central cavity. Tentacles are used in capturing food and in performing a certain type of locomotion, much like a "handspring." To accomplish this motion, the hydra attaches its tentacles to the substrate and flips the basal portion of its body completely over, reattaching the base to a new position. If water fleas (*Daphnia*) are available, place one or two near the tentacles of the hydra and note the hydra's behavior. Set aside the hydra in the depression slide and return to it in a few moments.

2. Study a prepared slide of *Hydra* sections using the compound microscope and compare your observations with Figure 3b and c.

   Are definite tissue layers present? If so, how many?

   Given what you know of embryology, what embryonic layers would you guess give rise to the tissue layers of this animal's body?

3. Not visible with the microscope is a network of nerve cells in the body wall, which serves as the nervous system. There is no concentration of nerve cells into any kind of brain or nerve cord.

4. Observe the central cavity, called a **gastrovascular cavity.** Digestion begins in this water-filled cavity (**extracellular digestion**), but many food particles are drawn into cells in the **gastrodermis** lining the cavity, where **intracellular digestion** occurs.

5. Do you see signs of a skeleton or supportive system? How do you think the body is supported? Are appendages present?

6. Recalling the whole organism and observing this cross section, are organs for gas exchange present? How is gas exchange accomplished?

7. Do you see any organs for excretion?

8. Are specialized cell types seen in the layers of tissues?

Cnidarians have a unique cell type called **cnidocytes,** which contain a stinging organelle called a **nematocyst.** When stimulated, the nematocyst will evert from the cnidocyte with explosive force, trapping food or stinging predators. Look for these cells.

9. To better observe cnidocytes and nematocysts, turn your attention again to your living hydra and follow this procedure:

   a. Using a pipette, transfer the hydra to a drop of water on a microscope slide and carefully add a coverslip.

   b. Use your microscope to examine the hydra, first on low, then intermediate, and finally on high powers, focusing primarily on the tentacles. The cnidocytes will appear as swellings. If your microscope is equipped with phase contrast, switch to phase. Alternatively, add a drop of methylene blue to the edge of the coverslip. Locate several cnidocytes with nematocysts coiled inside.

   c. Add a drop of 1% acetic acid to the edge of the coverslip and, watching carefully using intermediate power, observe the rapid discharge of the nematocyst from the cnidocyte.

   d. Using high power, study the discharged nematocysts that will appear as long threads, often with large spines, or barbs, at the base of the thread.

Results

Complete the summary table, recording all information for *Hydra* characteristics in the appropriate row.

Discussion

What major differences have you detected between *Scypha* and *Hydra* body forms? List and describe them.

EXERCISE 3
Phylum Platyhelminthes— Planarians (*Dugesia*)

Materials

stereoscopic microscope
compound microscope
living planarian
watch glass

prepared slide of whole mount of planarian
prepared slide of planarian cross sections

Introduction

Planarians are free-living flatworms; that is, they are not parasitic and their body is dorsoventrally flattened. They are found under rocks, leaves, and debris in freshwater ponds and creeks. They move over these surfaces using a combination of muscles in their body wall and cilia on their ventral sides.

Procedure

1. Add a dropperful of pond or culture water to a watch glass. Use a dropper to obtain a living planarian from the class culture. Using your stereoscopic microscope, observe the planarian. Describe its locomotion. Is it directional? What is the position of its head? Does its body appear to contract?

    As you observe the living planarian, you will see two striking new features with regard to symmetry that you did not see in the two phyla previously studied. What are they?

Figure 4.
A planarian. The digestive system consists of a mouth, a pharynx, and a branched intestine. A brain and two ventral nerve cords (plus transverse nerves connecting them, not shown) make up the nervous system.

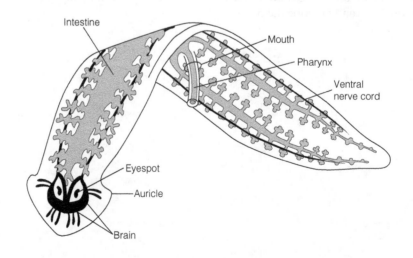

2. Add a *small* piece of fresh liver to the water near the planarian. The planarian may approach the liver and begin to feed by extending a long tubular **pharynx** out of the **mouth,** a circular opening on the ventral side of the body. If the planarian feeds, it will curve its body over the liver and extend the pharynx, which may be visible in the stereoscopic microscope.

   After observing the planarian's feeding behavior, return it to the culture dish, if possible, without the liver.

3. Using the lowest power on the compound microscope, observe the prepared slide of a whole planarian and compare it with Figure 4.

Do not observe these slides using high power! The high power objective may crack the coverslip, resulting in damage to the lens.

 ─────────────────────────────

Examine the body for possible digestive tract openings. How many openings to the digestive tract are present?

Observe again the pharynx and the mouth. The pharynx lies in a **pharyngeal chamber** inside the mouth. The proximal end of the pharynx opens into a dark-colored, branched intestine. If the intestine has been stained on your slide, you will see the branching more easily.

4. Continue your study of the whole planarian. The anterior blunt end of the animal is the head end. At each side of the head is a projecting **auricle.** It contains a variety of sensory cells, chiefly of touch and chemical sense. Between the two auricles on the dorsal surface are two pigmented **eyespots.** These are pigment cups into which retinal cells extend from the brain, with the photosensitive end of the cells inside the cup. Eyespots are sensitive to light intensities and the direction of a light source but can form no images. Beneath the eyespots are two cerebral ganglia that serve as the **brain.** Two ventral nerve cords extend posteriorly from the brain. These are connected by transverse nerves to form a ladderlike **nervous system.**

5. Study the prepared slide of cross sections of a planarian. You will have several sections on one slide. One section should have been taken at the level of the pharynx and pharyngeal chamber. Do you see a body cavity in any of the sections? (The pharyngeal chamber and spaces in the gut are not a body cavity.) What word describes this body cavity condition (see Figure 1a)?

a. How many tissue layers can be detected? Speculate about their embryonic origin.

Flatworms are the first group of animals to have three well-defined embryonic tissue layers, enabling them to have a variety of tissues and organs. Reproductive organs and excretory organs consisting of two lateral excretory canals and "flame cells" that move fluid through the canals are derived from the embryonic mesoderm. Respiratory, circulatory, and skeletal systems are lacking.

b. How do you think the body is supported?

c. How does gas exchange take place?

Results

1. Diagram the flatworm as seen in a cross section at the level of the pharynx. Label the **epidermis, muscle** derived from **mesoderm,** the lining of the digestive tract derived from **endoderm,** the **pharynx,** and the **pharyngeal chamber.**

2. Complete the summary table, recording all information for planarian characteristics in the appropriate row.

Discussion

One of the major differences between Cnidaria and Platyhelminthes is radial versus bilateral symmetry. Discuss the advantage of radial symmetry for sessile (attached) animals and bilateral symmetry for motile animals.

EXERCISE 4

Phylum Nematoda— Roundworms (*Ascaris*)

Materials

dissecting instruments
dissecting pan
dissecting pins
compound microscope
disposable gloves

preserved *Ascaris*
prepared slide of cross section
    of *Ascaris*
hand lens (optional)

Introduction

Ascaris is a **roundworm,** or nematode, that lives as a parasite in the intestines of mammals such as horses, pigs, and humans. Most often these parasites are introduced into the mammalian body when food contaminated with nematode eggs is eaten. Keep in mind the problem of adaptation to a parasitic lifestyle as you study the structure of this animal.

 Wear gloves while dissecting preserved animals.

Procedure

1. Wearing disposable gloves, obtain a preserved *Ascaris* and determine its sex. Females are generally larger than males. The posterior end of the male is sharply curved.

2. Use a hand lens or a stereoscopic microscope to look at the ends of the worm. A mouth is present at the anterior end. Three "lips" border this opening. A small slitlike **anus** is located ventrally near the posterior end of the animal.

3. Open the animal by making a middorsal incision along the length of the body with a sharp-pointed probe or sharp scissors. Remember that the anus is slightly to the ventral side (Figure 5). Be careful not to go too deep. Once the animal is open, pin the free edges of the body wall

Figure 5.
Male and female *Ascaris.*
The digestive tract originates at the mouth and terminates in the anus. Reproductive structures fill the body cavity.

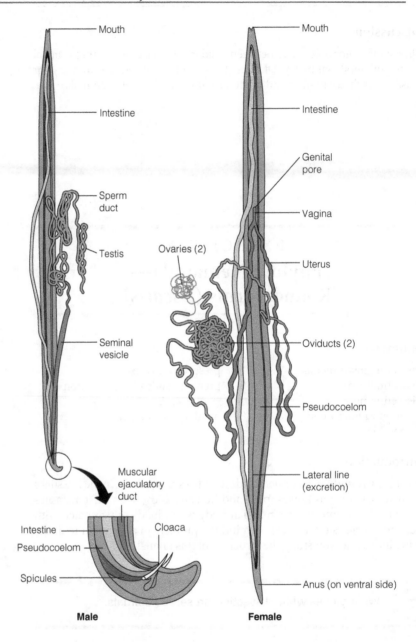

to the dissecting pan, spreading open the body. Pinning the animal near the edge of the pan will allow you to view it using the stereoscopic microscope. As you study the internal organs, you will note that there is a **body cavity.** This is not a true coelom, however, as you will see shortly when you study microscopic sections. From your observations, you should readily identify such characteristics as symmetry, tissue organization, and digestive tract openings.

a. The most obvious organs you will see in the dissected worm are **reproductive organs,** which appear as masses of coiled tubules of varying diameters.

b. Identify the flattened **digestive tract,** or intestine, extending from mouth to anus. This tract has been described as a "tube within a tube," the outer tube being the body wall.

c. Locate two pale lines running laterally along the length of the body in the body wall. The excretory system consists of two longitudinal tubes lying in these two **lateral lines.**

d. There are no organs for gas exchange or circulation. Most parasitic roundworms are essentially anaerobic (require no oxygen).

e. How would nourishment be taken into the body and be circulated?

f. The nervous system consists of a ring of nervous tissue around the anterior end of the worm, with one dorsal and one ventral nerve cord. These structures will be more easily observed in the prepared slide.

g. Do you see signs of segmentation in the body wall or in the digestive, reproductive, or excretory systems?

h. Do you see signs of a support system? What do you think supports the body?

4. Using the compound microscope, observe a prepared slide of a cross section through the body of a female worm. Note that the body wall is made up of (from outside inward) **cuticle** (noncellular), **epidermis** (cellular), and **muscle fibers.** The muscle (derived from mesoderm) lies at the outer boundary of the body cavity. Locate the **intestine** (derived from endoderm). Can you detect muscle tissue adjacent to the endodermal layer?

What do we call a coelom that is lined by mesoderm (outside) and endoderm (inside) (see Figure 1b)?

5. Most of the body cavity is filled with reproductive organs. You should see cross sections of the two large **uteri,** sections of the coiled **oviducts** with small lumens, and many sections of the **ovaries** with no lumen. What do you see inside the uteri?

6. By carefully observing the cross section, you should be able to locate the **lateral lines** for excretion and the dorsal and ventral **nerve cords.**

Results

1. Sketch the cross section of a female *Ascaris*. Label the **cuticle, epidermis, muscle fibers, intestine, body cavity** (give specific name), **reproductive organs, (uterus, oviduct, ovary), lateral lines,** and **dorsal** and **ventral nerve cords.**

2. List some features of *Ascaris* that are possible adaptations to parasitic life.

3. Complete the summary table, recording all information for roundworm characteristics in the appropriate row.

Discussion

1. Discuss the significance of an animal's having two separate openings to the digestive tract, as seen in *Ascaris*.

2. What are the advantages of a body cavity being present in an animal?

EXERCISE 5

Phylum Annelida—Clamworms (*Nereis*) and Earthworms (*Lumbricus terrestris*)

The phylum Annelida includes a diverse group of organisms inhabiting a variety of environments. Examples range in size from microscopic to several meters in length. Most species are marine, living free in the open ocean or burrowing in ocean bottoms. Others live in fresh water or in soils. One group of annelids, the leeches, are parasitic and live on the blood or tissues of their hosts. In this exercise, you will study the clamworm, a marine annelid, and the earthworm, a terrestrial species. Keep in mind features that are adaptations to marine and terrestrial habitats as you study these organisms.

Lab Study A. Clamworms (*Nereis*)

Materials

dissecting tools   disposable gloves
dissecting pan   dissecting pins
preserved clamworm

Introduction

Species of *Nereis* (clamworms) are commonly found in mud flats and on the ocean floor. These animals burrow in sediments during the day and emerge to feed at night. As you observe the clamworm, note features that are characteristic of all annelids, as well as features that are special adaptations to the marine environment.

Procedure

1. Observe the preserved, undissected clamworm and compare it with Figure 6. How would you describe the symmetry of this organism?

2. Determine the anterior and posterior ends. At the anterior end, the well-differentiated head bears **sensory appendages.** Locate the mouth, which leads into the digestive tract.

Figure 6.
The clamworm, *Nereis*. The head has sensory appendages, and each segment of the body bears two parapodia with setae.

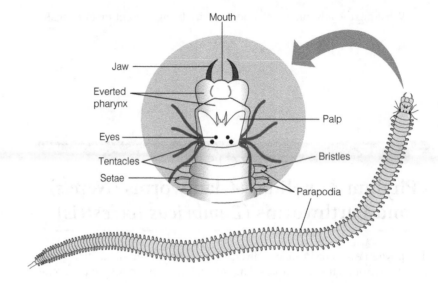

3. A conspicuous new feature of these organisms is the presence of **segmentation,** the division of the body along its length into segments. Posterior to the head region, the segments bear fleshy outgrowths called **parapodia.** Each parapodium contains several terminal bristles called **setae.** In Lab Study B, you will see that the earthworm has setae but does not have parapodia. Suggest functions for parapodia and setae in the marine clamworm.

4. Holding the animal in your hand and using sharp-pointed scissors, make a middorsal incision the full length of the body. Carefully insert the tip of the scissors and lift up with the tips as you cut. Pin the opened body in the dissecting pan but do not put pins through the head region.

5. Locate the **intestine.** Do you see the "tube-within-a-tube" body plan?

6. Two **muscle layers,** one inside the skin and a second lying on the surface of the intestine, may be visible with the stereoscopic microscope. With muscle in these two positions, what kind of coelom does this animal have (see Figure 1c)?

7. Continuing your observations with the unaided eye and the stereoscopic microscope, look for **blood vessels,** particularly a large vessel lying on the dorsal wall of the digestive tract. This vessel is contractile and pro-

pels the blood throughout the body. You should be able to observe smaller lateral blood vessels connecting the dorsal blood vessel with another on the ventral side of the intestine. As you will see, in the earthworm these connecting vessels are slightly enlarged as "hearts" around the anterior portion of the digestive tract (around the esophagus). This is not as obvious in *Nereis*. What is this type of circulatory system, with blood circulating through continuous closed vessels?

8. Gas exchange must take place across wet, thin surfaces. Do you see any organs for gas exchange (gills or lungs, for example)? How do you suspect that gas exchange takes place?

9. Do you see any signs of a skeleton? What would serve as support for the body?

10. Clamworms and earthworms have a small bilobed brain (a pair of ganglia) lying on the surface of the digestive tract at the anterior end of the worm. You can see this more easily in an earthworm.

Lab Study B. Earthworms (*Lumbricus terrestris*)

Materials

dissecting instruments
compound microscope
stereoscopic microscope

preserved earthworm
prepared slide of cross section
  of earthworm

Introduction

Lumbricus species, commonly called *earthworms*, burrow through soils rich in organic matter. As you observe these animals, note features that are adaptations to the burrowing, terrestrial lifestyle.

Procedure

1. Obtain a preserved earthworm and identify its anterior end by locating the mouth, which is overhung by a fleshy dorsal protuberance called the **prostomium.** The anus at the posterior end has no such protuberance. Also, a swollen glandular band, the **clitellum** (a structure that secretes a cocoon that holds eggs), is located closer to the mouth than to the anus (Figure 7).

   a. Using scissors, make a middorsal incision along the anterior third of the animal, as you did for *Nereis*. You can identify the dorsal surface in a couple of ways. The prostomium is dorsal, and the ventral surface

Figure 7.

The earthworm. The small brain leads to a ventral nerve cord. A pair of nephridia lie in each segment.

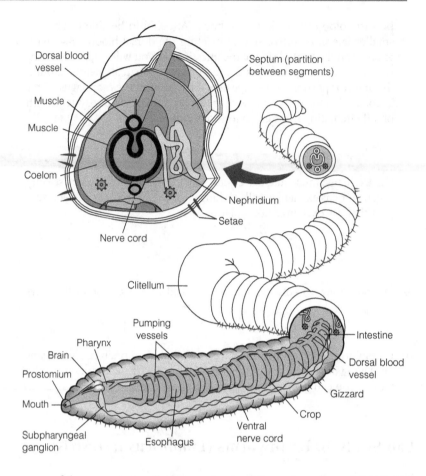

Dorsal blood vessel

Muscle

Muscle

Coelom

Nerve cord

Septum (partition between segments)

Nephridium

Setae

Clitellum

Pumping vessels

Pharynx

Brain

Prostomium

Mouth

Subpharyngeal ganglion

Esophagus

Ventral nerve cord

Crop

Gizzard

Dorsal blood vessel

Intestine

of the worm is usually flattened, especially in the region of the clitellum. Cut to the prostomium. Pin the body open in a dissecting pan near the edge. You may need to cut through the septa that divide the body cavity into segments.

b. Using a stereoscopic microscope or hand lens, look for the small **brain** just behind the prostomium on the surface of the digestive tract. Note the two nerves that pass from the brain around the pharynx and meet ventrally. These nerve tracts continue posteriorly as a **ventral nerve cord** lying in the floor of the coelom.

c. Look for the large **blood vessel** on the dorsal wall of the digestive tract. You may be able to see the enlarged lateral blood vessels (**hearts**) around the anterior portion of the digestive tract.

d. Identify (from anterior to posterior) the **pharynx, esophagus, crop** (a soft, swollen region of the digestive tract), **gizzard** (smaller and more rigid than the crop), and **intestine.**

e. Excretion in the clamworm and earthworm is carried out by organs called **nephridia.** A pair of these minute, white, coiled tubes is located in each segment of the worm body. Nephridia are more easily observed in the earthworm than in *Nereis* and should be studied here. To view these organs, cut out an approximately 2-cm-long piece of the worm posterior to the clitellum and cut it open along its dorsal surface. Cut through the septa and pin the piece to the dissecting pan near the edge to facilitate observation with the stereoscopic microscope. The coiled tubules of the nephridia are located in the coelomic cavity, where waste is collected and discharged to the outside through a small pore.

2. Using the compound microscope, observe the prepared slide of a cross section of the earthworm.

   a. Locate the **thin cuticle** lying outside of and secreted by the **epidermis.** Recall the habitat of this organism and speculate about the function of the cuticle.

   b. Confirm your decision about the type of coelom by locating **muscle layers** inside the epidermis and also lying on the surface of the **intestine** near the body cavity.

   c. Locate the **ventral nerve cord,** lying in the floor of the coelom, just inside the muscle layer.

Results

Complete the summary table, recording all information for clamworm and earthworm characteristics in the appropriate row.

Discussion

A major new feature observed in the phylum Annelida is the segmented body. Speculate about possible adaptive advantages provided by segmentation.

By the end of today's laboratory period, you should have completed observations of all animals described in Animal Diversity I. The next lab topic, Animal Diversity II, is a continuation of this investigation and will present similar laboratory objectives. In Animal Diversity II, you will continue asking questions and making comparisons as you did in Animal Diversity I. By the end of the two lab topics, you should be able to use what you have learned about the animals to discuss and answer questions about the unifying themes of these laboratory topics.

Applying your Knowledge

A hydra (*Chlorophyra viridissima*) is bright green, and yet it does not synthesize chlorophyll. Think about the structure of the hydra and its feeding and digestive habits. What do you think is the origin of the green pigment in this species?

References

Balavoine, G. "Are Platyhelminthes Coelomates Without a Coelom? An Argument Based on the Evolution of Hox Genes," *American Zoologist,* 1989, vol. 38, pp. 843–858.

Bond, C. "Keeping Up with the Sponges," *Natural History,* 1998, vol. 106, pp. 22–25.

Erwin, D., J. Valentine, and D. Jablonski. "The Origin of Animal Body Plans," *American Scientist,* 1997, vol. 85, pp. 126–137.

Website

Includes descriptions of many invertebrates and vertebrates, links to insect keys, references:

http://animaldiversity.ummz.umich.edu/index.html

Art Credits

1: Adapted from Neil Campbell, *Biology,* 4th ed. (Menlo Park, CA: Benjamin/Cummings, 1996), ©1996 The Benjamin/Cummings Publishing Company. 2, 3: Adapted from Larry Mitchell, John Mutchmor, and Warren Dolphin, *Zoology* (Menlo Park, CA: Benjamin/Cummings, 1988), ©1988 The Benjamin/Cummings Publishing Company. 4: Adapted from Neil Campbell, Jane Reece, and Larry Mitchell, *Biology,* 5th ed. (Menlo Park, CA: Benjamin/Cummings, 1999), ©1999 The Benjamin/ Cummings Publishing Company. 5: Adapted from Larry Mitchell, John Mutchmor, and Warren Dolphin, *Zoology* (Menlo Park, CA: Benjamin/Cummings, 1988), ©1988 The Benjamin/Cummings Publishing Company. 7: Adapted from Neil Campbell, Jane Reece, and Larry Mitchell, *Biology,* 5th ed. (Menlo Park, CA: Benjamin/ Cummings, 1999), ©1999 The Benjamin/Cummings Publishing Company.

Animal Diversity II

 This lab is a continuation of observations of organisms in the animal kingdom as discussed in Animal Diversity I.

As you continue your study of representative organisms, continue to record your observations in Table 1 at the end of this lab topic. Keep in mind the big themes you are investigating.

1. What clues do similarities and differences among organisms provide about phylogenetic relationships?
2. How is body form related to function?
3. How is body form related to environment and lifestyle?
4. What characteristics can be the criteria for major branching points in producing a phylogenetic tree (representing animal classification)?

EXERCISE 1
Phylum Mollusca—Clams

Materials

dissecting instruments
dissecting pan

preserved clam or mussel
disposable gloves

Introduction

Second only to the phylum Arthropoda in numbers of species, the phylum Mollusca includes thousands of species living in many diverse habitats. Most species are marine. Others live in fresh water or on land. Many mollusks are of economic importance, being favorite human foods. Most mollusks share four characteristic features: (1) a hard external **shell** for protection; (2) a thin structure called the **mantle**, which secretes the shell; (3) a **visceral mass** in which most organs are located; and (4) a muscular **foot** used for locomotion.

From *Investigating Biology*, Fourth Edition, Judith Giles Morgan and M. Eloise Brown Carter. Copyright © 2002 Pearson Education, Inc., publishing as Benjamin Cummings. All rights reserved.

In this exercise, you will dissect a clam, a molluscan species with a shell made of two parts called **valves**. Most clams are marine, although many genera live in freshwater lakes and ponds.

 Wear gloves while dissecting preserved animals.

Procedure

1. Observe the external anatomy of the preserved clam. Certain characteristics will become obvious immediately. Can you determine symmetry, support systems, and the presence or absence of appendages? Are there external signs of segmentation? Record observations in Table 1.

2. Before you continue making observations, determine the dorsal, ventral, anterior, posterior, right, and left regions of the animal. Identify the two valves. The valves are held together by a **hinge** near the **umbo,** a hump on the valves. The hinge and the umbo are located **dorsally,** and the valves open **ventrally.** The umbo is displaced **anteriorly.** Hold the clam vertically with the umbo away from your body, and cup one of your hands over each valve. The valve in your right hand is the right valve; the valve in your left hand is the left valve. The two valves are held together by two strong **adductor** muscles inside the shell. Compare your observations with Figure 1.

 Be cautious as you open the clam! Hold the clam in the dissecting pan in such a way that the scalpel will be directed toward the bottom of the pan.

Figure 1.
Anatomy of a clam. The soft body parts are protected by the shell valves. Two adductor muscles hold the valves closed. Most major organs are located in the visceral mass. In this diagram, the left mantle, left pair of gills, and half of the visceral mass have been removed.

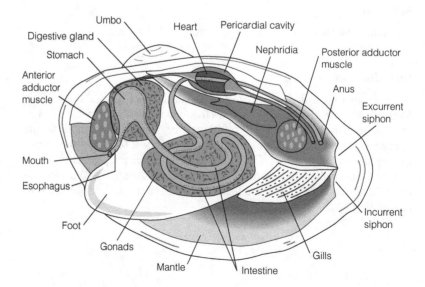

116

3. To study the internal anatomy of the clam, you must open it by prying open the valves. (A wooden peg may have been inserted between the two valves.) Insert the handle of your forceps or scalpel between the valves and twist it to pry the valves farther open. Carefully insert a scalpel blade, directed toward the dorsal side of the animal, into the space between the left valve and a flap of tissue lining the valve. The blade edge should be just ventral to (that is, below) the anterior adductor muscle (see Figure 1). The flap of tissue is the left **mantle.** Keeping the scalpel blade pressed flat against the left valve, carefully loosen the mantle from the valve and press the blade dorsally. You will feel the tough **anterior adductor muscle.** Cut through this muscle near the valve.

4. Repeat the procedure at the posterior end and cut the posterior adductor muscle. Lay the clam on its right valve and carefully lift the left valve. As you do this, use your scalpel to loosen the mantle from the valve. If you have been successful, you should have the body of the clam lying in the right valve. It should be covered by the mantle. Look for pearls between the mantle and the shell. How do you think pearls are formed?

5. Look at the posterior end of the animal where the left and right mantle come together. Hold the two mantle flaps together and note the two gaps formed. These gaps are called **incurrent** (ventral) and **excurrent** (dorsal) **siphons.** Speculate about the function of these siphons.

6. Lift the mantle and identify the **visceral mass** and the **muscular foot.**

7. Locate the **gills,** which have a pleated appearance. One function of these structures is obvious, but they have a second function as well. As water comes into the body (how would it get in?), it passes through the gills, and food particles are trapped on the gill surface. The food is then moved anteriorly (toward the mouth) by coordinated ciliary movements.

8. Locate the **mouth** between two flaps of tissue just ventral to the anterior adductor muscle. Look just above the posterior adductor muscle and locate the **anus.** How is it oriented in relation to the excurrent siphon?

9. Imagine that this is the first time you have seen a clam. From the observations you have made, what evidence would indicate whether this animal is aquatic or terrestrial?

10. The **heart** of the clam is located in a sinus, or cavity, just inside the hinge, dorsal to the visceral mass (see Figure 1). This cavity, called the *pericardial cavity,* is a reduced **true coelom.** The single ventricle of the

heart actually surrounds the **intestine** passing through this cavity. Thin auricles, usually torn away during the dissection, empty into the heart via openings called **ostia.** Blood passes from **sinuses** in the body into the auricles. What type of circulatory system is this?

11. Ventral to the heart and embedded in mantle tissue are a pair of greenish brown tissue masses, the **nephridia,** or kidneys. The kidneys remove waste from the pericardial cavity.

12. Open the visceral mass by making an incision with the scalpel, dividing the mass into right and left halves. Begin this incision just above the foot and cut dorsally. You should be able to open the flap produced by this cut and see organs such as the **gonads, digestive gland, intestine,** and **stomach.** Clam chowder is made by chopping up the visceral mass.

13. It is difficult to observe the nervous system in the clam. It consists of three ganglia, one near the mouth, one in the foot, and one below the posterior adductor muscle. These ganglia are connected by nerves.

Now that you have dissected the clam, you should have concluded that there is no sign of true segmentation. Also, appendages (attached to a trunk or body wall) are absent.

Results

Complete Summary Table 1, recording all information for clam characteristics in the appropriate row. Use this information to answer questions in the Applying Your Knowledge section at the end of this lab topic.

Discussion

List several features of clam anatomy that enable it to survive in a marine environment.

EXERCISE 2
Phylum Arthropoda

Organisms in the phylum Arthropoda have been very successful species. Evidence indicates that arthropods may have lived on Earth half a billion years ago. They can be found in almost every imaginable habitat: marine waters, fresh water, and almost every terrestrial niche. Many species are directly beneficial to humans, serving as a source of food. Others make humans miserable by eating their homes, infesting their domestic animals, eating their food, and biting their bodies. In this exercise, you will observe the morphology of two arthropods: the crayfish (an aquatic arthropod) and the grasshopper (a terrestrial arthropod).

Lab Study A. Crayfish (*Cambarus*)

Materials

dissecting instruments   preserved crayfish
dissecting pan   disposable gloves

Introduction

Crayfish live in streams, ponds, and swamps, usually protected under rocks and vegetation. They may walk slowly over the substrate of their habitat, but they can also swim rapidly using their tails. The segmentation seen in annelids is seen also in crayfish and all arthropods; however, you will see that the segments are grouped into functional units.

Procedure

1. Obtain a preserved crayfish, study its external anatomy, and compare your observations with Figure 2. Describe the body symmetry, supportive structures, appendages, and segmentation, and state the adaptive advantages of each characteristic.

   a. body symmetry

   b. supportive structures

   c. appendages

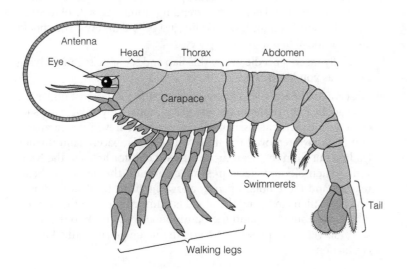

Figure 2.
External anatomy of a crayfish.
The body is divided into head, thorax, and abdominal regions. Appendages grouped in a region perform specific functions.

d. segmentation

2. Identify the three regions of the crayfish body: the **head, thorax** (fused with the head), and **abdomen.** Note the appendages associated with each region. Speculate about the functions of each of these groups of appendages.

   a. head appendages

   b. thoracic appendages

   c. abdominal appendages

3. Feathery **gills** lie under the lateral extensions of a large, expanded exoskeletal plate called the **carapace** (see Figure 2). To expose the gills, use scissors to cut away a portion of the plate on the left side of the animal. What is the function of the gills? Speculate about how this function is performed.

4. Remove the dorsal portion of the carapace to observe other organs in the head and thorax. Compare your observations with Figure 3.

   a. Start on each side of the body at the posterior lateral edge of the carapace and make two lateral cuts extending along each side of the thorax and forward over the head, meeting just behind the eyes. This should create a dorsal flap in the carapace.

   b. Carefully insert a needle under this flap and separate the underlying tissues as you lift the flap.

   c. Observe the **heart,** a small, angular structure located just under the carapace near the posterior portion of the thorax. (If you were not successful in leaving the tissues behind as you removed the carapace, you may have removed the heart with the carapace.) Thin threads leading out from the heart are **arteries.** Look for holes in the heart wall. When blood collects in **sinuses** around the heart, the heart relaxes, and these holes open to allow the heart to fill with blood. The holes then close, and the blood is pumped through the arteries, which distribute it around the body. Blood seeps back to the heart, since no veins are present. What is the name given to this kind of circulation?

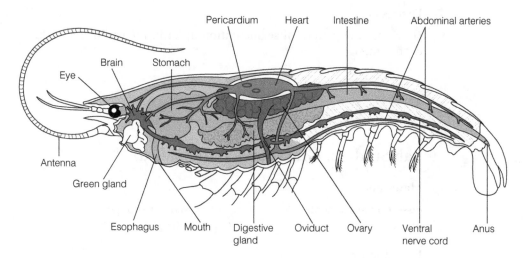

Figure 3.
Internal anatomy of the crayfish. Large digestive glands fill much of the body cavity. The intestine extends from the stomach through the tail to the anus. The green glands lie near the brain in the head.

 d. Locate the **stomach** in the head region. It is a large, saclike structure. It may be obscured by the large, white **digestive glands** that fill the body cavity inside the body wall. Leading posteriorly from the stomach is the **intestine.** Make longitudinal cuts through the exoskeleton on either side of the dorsal midline of the abdomen. Lift the exoskeleton and trace the intestine to the anus. (When shrimp are "deveined" in preparation for eating, the intestine is removed.) Given all of the organs and tissues around the digestive tract and inside the body wall in the body cavity, what kind of coelom do you think this animal has?

 e. Turn your attention to the anterior end of the specimen again. Pull the stomach posteriorly (this will tear the esophagus) and look inside the most anterior portion of the head. Two **green glands** (they do not look green), the animal's excretory organs, are located in this region. These are actually long tubular structures that resemble nephridia but are compacted into a glandular mass. Waste and excess water pass from these glands to the outside of the body through pores at the base of the antennae on the head.

 f. Observe the **brain** just anterior to the green glands. It lies in the midline with nerves extending posteriorly, fusing to form a **ventral nerve cord.**

Results

Complete Table 1, recording all information for crayfish characteristics in the appropriate row. Use this information to answer questions in the Applying Your Knowledge section at the end of this lab topic.

Discussion

How does the pattern of segmentation differ in the crayfish and the earthworm?

Lab Study B. Grasshoppers (*Romalea*)

Materials

dissecting instruments   preserved grasshopper
dissecting pan   disposable gloves

Introduction

The grasshopper, an insect, is an example of a terrestrial arthropod. Insects are the most successful and abundant of all land animals. They are the principal invertebrates in dry environments, and they can survive extreme temperatures. They are the only invertebrates that can fly. As you study the grasshopper, compare the anatomy of this terrestrial animal with that of the aquatic crayfish, just studied. This comparison should suggest ways that terrestrial animals have solved the problems of life out of water.

Procedure

1. Observe the external anatomy of the grasshopper. Compare your observations with Figure 4.

    a. Note the symmetry, supportive structures, appendages, and segmentation of the grasshopper.

Figure 4.
External anatomy of the grasshopper. The body is divided into head, thorax, and abdominal regions. Wings and large legs are present. Small openings, called *spiracles,* lead to internal tracheae, allowing air to pass into the body.

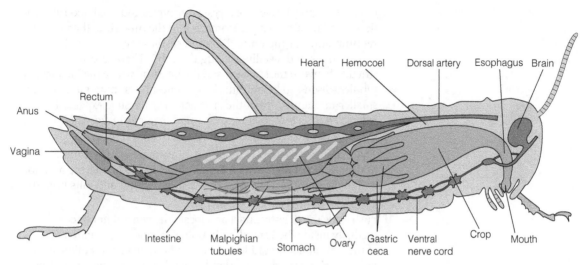

Figure 5.
Internal anatomy of the grasshopper. The digestive tract, extending from mouth to anus, is divided into specialized regions: the esophagus, crop, stomach, intestine, and rectum. Gastric ceca attach at the junction of the crop and the stomach. Malpighian tubules empty excretory waste into the anterior end of the intestine.

    b. Observe the body parts. The body is divided into three regions: the **head,** the **thorax** (to which the legs and wings are attached), and the **abdomen.** Examine the appendages on the head, speculate about their functions, and locate the mouth opening into the digestive tract.

    c. Turning your attention to the abdomen, locate small dots along each side. These dots are **spiracles,** small openings into elastic air tubes, or **tracheae,** that branch to all parts of the body and constitute the respiratory system of the grasshopper. This system of tubes brings oxygen directly to the cells of the body.

2. Remove the exoskeleton. First take off the wings and, starting at the posterior end, use scissors to make two lateral cuts toward the head. Remove the dorsal wall of the exoskeleton and note the segmented pattern in the muscles inside the body wall. Compare your observations with Figure 5 as you work.

    a. A space between the body wall and the digestive tract, the **hemocoel** (a true coelom), in life is filled with colorless blood. What type of circulation does the grasshopper have?

        The heart of a grasshopper is an elongate, tubular structure lying just inside the middorsal body wall. This probably will not be visible.

    b. Locate the digestive tract and again note the mouth. Along the length of the tract are regions specialized for specific functions. A narrow **esophagus** leading from the mouth expands into a large **crop** used for food storage. The crop empties into the **stomach,** where digestion takes place. Six pairs of fingerlike extensions called **gastric pouches** or **ceca** connect to the digestive tract where the crop and the stomach meet. These pouches secrete digestive enzymes and aid in food absorption. Food passes from the stomach into the **intestine,** then into the **rectum,** and out the **anus.** Distinguish these regions by observing constrictions and swellings along the tube. There is usually a constriction between the stomach and the intestine where the Malpighian tubules (discussed below) attach. The intestine is shorter and usually smaller in diameter than the stomach. *The intestine expands into an enlarged rectum that absorbs excess water from any undigested food, and relatively dry excrement passes out the anus.*

c. The excretory system is made up of numerous tiny tubules, the **Malpighian tubules,** which empty their products into the anterior end of the intestine. These tubules remove wastes and salts from the blood. Locate these tubules.

d. Push aside the digestive tract and locate the **ventral nerve cord** lying medially inside the ventral body wall. Ganglia are expanded regions of the ventral nerve cord found in each body segment. Following the nerve cord anteriorly, note that branches from the nerve cord pass around the digestive tract and meet, forming a brain in the head.

Results

Complete Table 1, recording all information for grasshopper characteristics in the appropriate row. Use this information to answer questions in the Applying Your Knowledge section at the end of this lab topic.

Discussion

1. Describe how each of the following external structures helps the grasshopper live successfully in terrestrial environments.
   a. Exoskeleton

   b. Wings

   c. Large, jointed legs

   d. Spiracles

2. Describe how each of the following internal structures helps the grasshopper live successfully in terrestrial environments.
   a. Tracheae

   b. Malpighian tubules

c. Rectum

EXERCISE 3
Phylum Chordata

The phylum Chordata includes another diverse group of organisms. Organisms in two subphyla of chordates are invertebrates, and animals in the largest subphylum have a bony or cartilaginous endoskeleton that includes a vertebral column and are called *vertebrates*. Chordates inhabit terrestrial and aquatic (freshwater and marine) environments. One group has developed the ability to fly. The body plan of chordates is unique in that these animals demonstrate a complex of four important characteristics at some stage in their development. In this exercise, you will discover these characteristics.

You will study two chordate species: the lancelet, an invertebrate in the subphylum Cephalochordata, and the pig, a vertebrate in the subphylum Vertebrata. The third subphylum, Urochordata, will not be studied.

Lab Study A. Lancelets (*Branchiostoma,* formerly *Amphioxus*)

Materials

compound microscope
stereoscopic microscope
preserved lancelet in watch glass

prepared slide of whole mount of lancelet
prepared slide of cross section of lancelet

Introduction

Lancelets are marine animals that burrow in sand in tidal flats. They feed with their head end extended from their burrow. They resemble fish superficially, but their head is poorly developed, and they have unique features not found in fish or other vertebrates. They retain the four unique characteristics of chordates throughout their life cycle and are excellent animals to use to demonstrate these features. In this lab study, you will observe preserved lancelets, prepared slides of whole mounts, and cross sections through the body of a lancelet.

Procedure

1. Place a preserved lancelet in water in a watch glass and observe it using the stereoscopic microscope. Handle the specimen with care and *do not dissect it*. Note the fishlike shape of the slender, elongate body. Locate the anterior end by the presence at that end of a noselike **rostrum** extending over the mouth region, surrounded by small tentacles. Notice the lack of a well-defined head. Look for the segmented muscles that surround much of the animal's body. Can you see signs of a tail? If the

125

animal you are studying is mature, you will be able to see two rows of 20 to 25 white gonads on the ventral surface of the body.

2. Return the specimen to the correct container.

3. Observe the whole mount slide of the lancelet and compare your observations with Figure 6.

 Use only the lowest power on the compound microscope to study this slide.

a. Scan the entire length of the body wall. Do you see evidence of segmentation in the muscles?

b. Look at the anterior end of the animal. Do you see evidence of a sensory system? Describe what you see.

c. Locate the mouth of the animal at the anterior end. See if you can follow a tube from just under the rostrum into a large sac with numerous gill slits. This sac is the **pharynx with gill slits,** a uniquely chordate structure. Water and food pass into the pharynx from the mouth. Food passes posteriorly from the pharynx into the intestine, which ends at the anus on the ventral side of the animal, several millimeters before the end. The extension of the body beyond the anus is called a **post-anal tail.** Think of the worms you studied in Animal Diversity I. Where was the anus located in these animals? Was a post-anal region present? Explain.

Figure 6.
The lancelet, whole mount. The rostrum extends over the mouth region. The pharynx, including the pharyngeal gill slits, leads to the intestine, which exits the body at the anus. Note that a tail extends beyond the anus. Structures positioned from the dorsal surface of the body inward include a dorsal fin, the nerve cord, and the notochord.

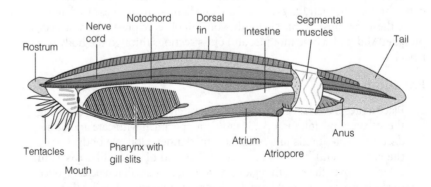

d. Water entering the mouth passes through the gill slits and collects in a chamber, the **atrium,** just inside the body wall. The water ultimately passes out of the body at a ventral pore, the **atripore.** Surprisingly, the gill slits are not the major gas exchange surface in the lancelet body. Because of the great activity of ciliated cells in this region, it is even possible that blood leaving the gill region has less oxygen than that entering the region. The function of gill slits is simply to strain food from the water. The major site for gas exchange is the body surface.

e. Now turn your attention to the dorsal side of the animal. Beginning at the surface of the body and moving inward, identify the listed structures and speculate about the function of each one.

dorsal fin:

nerve cord:

notochord:

The nerve cord is in a dorsal position. Have you seen only a dorsal nerve cord in any of the animals previously studied?

The notochord is a cartilage-like rod that lies ventral to the nerve cord and extends the length of the body. Have you seen a notochord in any of the previous animals?

The lancelet circulatory system is not visible in these preparations, but the animal has **closed circulation** with dorsal and ventral aortae, capillaries, and veins. Excretory organs, or nephridia (not visible here), are located near the true coelom, which surrounds the pharynx.

4. Observe the slide of cross sections taken through the lancelet body. There may be several sections on this slide, taken at several positions along the length of the body. Find the section through the pharynx and compare it with Figure 7.

 Study this slide on the lowest power.

Figure 7.
Cross section through the
pharyngeal region of the lancelet.

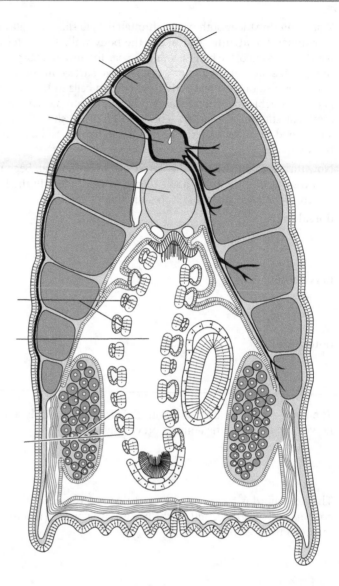

In cross section, it is much easier to see the structural relationships among the various organs of the lancelet. Identify the following structures and label them on Figure 7.

a. **Segmental muscles.** They are located on each side of the body, under the skin.

b. **Dorsal fin.** This projects upward from the most dorsal surface of the body.

c. **Nerve cord.** You may be able to see that the nerve cord contains a small central canal, thus making it hollow. The nerve cord is located in the dorsal region of the body, ventral to the dorsal fin between the lateral bundles of muscle.

d. **Notochord.** This is a large oval structure located just ventral to the nerve cord.

e. **Pharynx with gill slits.** This structure appears as a series of dark triangles arranged in an oval. The triangles are cross sections of **gill bars.** The spaces between the triangles are **gill slits,** through which water passes into the surrounding chamber.

Results

1. Complete the diagram of the lancelet cross section in Figure 7. Label all the structures listed in step 4 of the Procedure section.

2. Complete Table 1, recording all information for lancelet characteristics in the appropriate row. Use this information to answer questions in the Applying Your Knowledge section at the end of this lab topic.

Discussion

Describe the uniquely chordate features that you have detected in the lancelet that were not present in the animals previously studied.

Lab Study B. Fetal Pigs (*Sus scrofa*)

Materials

preserved fetal pig   disposable gloves
dissecting pan

Introduction

The pig is a terrestrial vertebrate. In this lab study, working with your lab partner, you will observe external features only, observing those characteristics studied in other animals in previous exercises. Compare the organization of the vertebrate body with the animals previously studied. As you dissect the pig in subsequent labs, come back to these questions and answer the ones that cannot be answered in today's lab study.

Procedure

1. Obtain a preserved fetal pig from the class supply and carry it to your desk in a dissecting pan.

 Use disposable gloves to handle preserved animals.

2. With your lab partner, read each of the following questions. Drawing on observations you have made of other animals in the animal diversity lab studies, predict the answer to each question about the fetal pig. Then examine the fetal pig and determine the answer, if possible. Give evidence for your answer based on your observations of the pig, your knowledge of vertebrate anatomy, or your understanding of animal phylogeny.

a. What type of symmetry does the pig body have?
Prediction:

Evidence:

b. How many layers of embryonic tissue are present?
Prediction:

Evidence:

c. Are cells organized into distinct tissues?
Prediction:

Evidence:

d. How many digestive tract openings are present? Would you describe this as a "tube within a tube"?
Prediction:

Evidence:

e. Is the circulatory system open or closed?
Prediction:

Evidence:

f. What is the habitat of the animal?
Prediction:

Evidence:

g. What are the organs for respiration?
   Prediction:

   Evidence:

h. What are the organs for excretion?
   Prediction:

   Evidence:

i. What is the method of locomotion?
   Prediction:

   Evidence:

j. Are support systems internal or external?
   Prediction:

   Evidence:

k. Is the body segmented?
   Prediction:

   Evidence:

l. Are appendages present?
Prediction:

Evidence:

m. What is the position and complexity of the nervous system?
Prediction:

Evidence:

Results

Complete Table 1, recording all information for pig characteristics in the appropriate row. Use this information to answer questions in the Applying Your Knowledge section that follows.

Results Summary

Complete the summary table, Table 1, recording in the appropriate row information about characteristics of all animals studied. Use this information to answer questions in the Applying Your Knowledge section that follows.

Applying Your Knowledge

1. Using specific examples from the animals you have studied, describe ways that organisms have adapted to specific environments.

    a. Compare organisms adapted to aquatic environments with those from terrestrial environments.

b. Compare adaptations of parasitic organisms with similar free-living organisms.

2. Using the summary table, Table 2, categorize the animals studied based on the 13 basic characteristics discussed previously.

3. Examine the phylogenetic tree in Figure 8 at the end of the topic, which illustrates evolutionary relationships among members of the animal kingdom. Each branching point on the tree represents a major characteristic that separates groups of organisms. For example, tissue organization (presence or absence of distinct tissue layers) separates sponges from all other animals. Based on your observations, select at least seven major criteria to be used for branching points in this phylogenetic tree. Write one criterion in the space provided at each branch point.

4. Upon superficial examination, the body form of certain present-day animals might be described as simple, yet these animals may have developed specialized structures, perhaps unique to their particular phylum. Illustrate this point using examples from some of the simpler organisms you have dissected.

5. From this lab, one might conclude that certain trends can be detected, trends from "primitive" features (those that arose early in the evolution of animals) to more "advanced" traits (those that arose later). However, animals with these alleged primitive characteristics still successfully exist on Earth today. Why is this so? Why have the more advanced animals not completely replaced the more primitive ones? Use examples from the lab to illustrate your answer.

6. A major theme in biology is the relationship between form and function in organisms. Select one of the major characteristics from Table 1, and illustrate the relationship of form and function for this characteristic using examples from the organisms studied.

Table 1

Summary Table of Animal Characteristics

Animal	Symmetry	Tissue Organization	Type of Body Cavity	Digestive Openings	Circulatory System	Habitat	Respiratory Organs
Sponge							
Hydra							
Planarian							
Roundworm							
Clamworm/ earthworm							
Clam							
Crayfish							
Grasshopper							
Lancelet							
Pig							

Table 1
Summary Table of Animal Characteristics (*continued*)

Animal	Excretory System	Locomotion	Support System	Segmentation	Appendages	Nervous System Organization
Sponge						
Hydra						
Planarian						
Roundworm						
Clamworm/ earthworm						
Clam						
Crayfish						
Grasshopper						
Lancelet						
Pig						

Table 2
Comparison of Organisms by Major Features

1. Tissue Organization a. distinct tissues absent: b. distinct tissues present:	**5. Circulatory System** a. none: b. open: c. closed:
2. Symmetry a. radial: b. bilateral:	**6. Habitat** a. aquatic: b. terrestrial: c. parasitic:
3. Body Cavity a. acoelomate: b. pseudocoelomate: c. eucoelomate:	**7. Organs for Gas Exchange** a. skin: b. gills: c. lungs: d. spiracles/tracheae:
4. Openings to Digestive Tract a. one: b. two:	

Table 2
Comparison of Organisms by Major Features *(continued)*

8. **Organs for Excretion** (list organ and animals)	11. **Segmented Body** a. no: b. yes:
	12. **Appendages** a. yes: b. no:
9. **Type of Locomotion** (list type and animals)	13. **Nervous System** a. ventral nerve cord: b. dorsal nerve cord: c. other:
10. **Support System** a. external: b. internal: c. hydrostatic:	

References

Hickman, C. P., L. S. Roberts, and A. Larson. *Integrated Principles of Zoology,* 10th ed. Dubuque, IA: Wm. C. Brown, 1997.

Zimmer, C. "An Explosion Defused?" *Discover,* 1996, vol. 17, p. 52.

Zimmer, C. "The Hidden Unity of Hearts," *Natural History,* (2000), vol. 109, pp. 56–60.

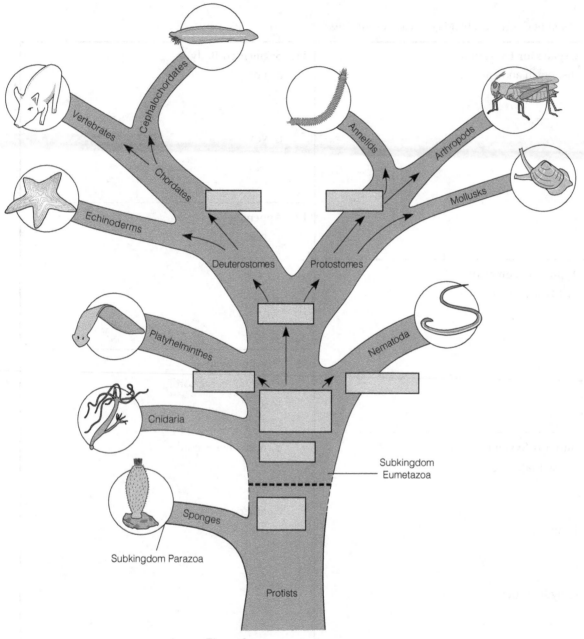

Figure 8.
Phylogenetic tree. Complete the figure by writing in the major criteria used to determine branching points.

Website

Includes descriptions of many invertebrates and vertebrates, links to insect keys, references:
http://animaldiversity.ummz.umich.edu/index.html

Art Credits

2, 3, 4, 6: Adapted from Larry Mitchell, John Mutchmor, and Warren Dolphin, *Zoology* (Menlo Park, CA: Benjamin/Cummings, 1988), ©1988 The Benjamin/Cummings Publishing Company.

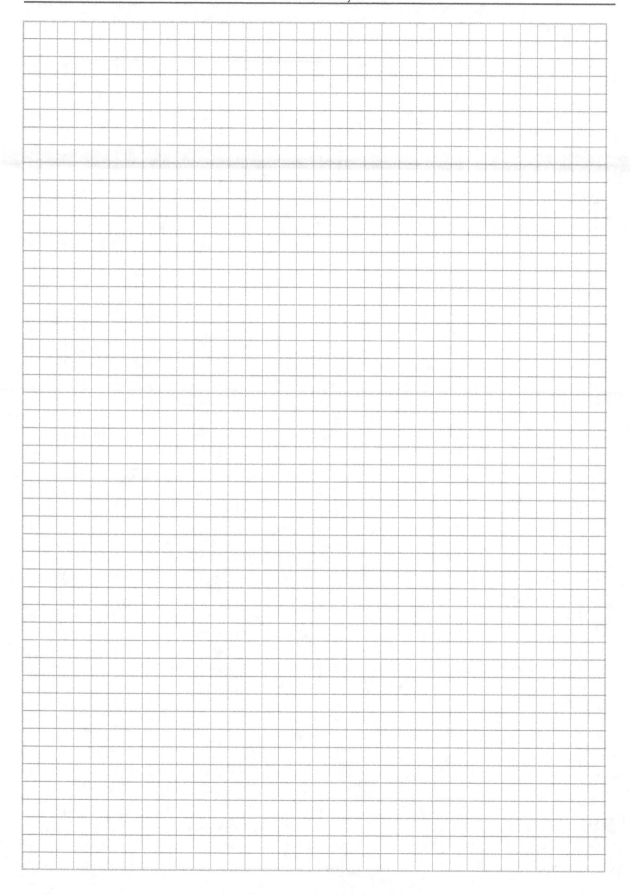